...all things are possible

yvonne duffy

Published by A.J. Garvin & Associates
Ann Arbor, Michigan

...all things are possible
by Yvonne Duffy

Published by:
A.J. Garvin and Associates
Post Office Box 7525
Ann Arbor, Mi 48107 U.S.A.

Copyright © 1981 by Yvonne Duffy
First Printing, December 1981
Printed in the United States of America

Library of Congress Catalog Card No. 81-83657

ISBN 0-9607252-0-2 Paperback

This book is dedicated to:
   William W. Scott, III, *who conceived
   the idea for this book,*
   Dr. Martin Kafka, *who supported me
   through the pangs of its birth,*
   Alexander J. Garvin, *who provided
   the means for its delivery,*
         and
   God, *through Whom All Things are Possible.*

Table of Contents

Acknowledgements

Although my name is on the cover, this book is the product of many persons. To the seventy-seven women who were the subjects of this study, I extend my deepest thanks not just for their time in answering such a lengthly questionnaire but also for their candid and thoughtful responses to even the most probing questions.

I would also like to thank Alice Mailhot and K Gordon for editing and proofreading the manuscript as well as for their consistent encouragement and support.

Here at the University of Michigan, my appreciation goes to the Lesbian Advocate's Office for its release of Patricia Myers to transcribe tapes and type a portion of the manuscript and the staff at the Office of Disabled Student Services for the many ways they have assisted throughout the project.

This book could not have been completed without the faithful aid of: Celia Easton, K Gordon, Laura Lowy, Shirin Moezzi, Nancy Scott, and Nancy Sparrow-Bray for coding responses to the 152 questions of the questionnaire; Jean Boettcher, Patricia Dickinson, Deidre Feeney, Wendy Jans, and Theresa Reagan in typing several drafts of the manuscript; Rhonda Smith in preparation of the Glossary; and friends and helpers too numerous to mention individually who have gone beyond the call of duty in doing whatever has been necessary to keep the work flowing.

Nor could it have been completed without the tender support of the important man in my life, James C. Austin, who has taught me much about loving and giving.

I am grateful to the copyright holders acknowledged below for allowing me to use their work:

Lael Cappaert, for permission to quote from her book, **And God Said No**

Columbia University Press, for permission to quote from **Touching** by Ashley Montagu

Elaine Strauss, for permission to quote from her book, **In My Heart I'm Still Dancing**

Anet McConel, for her song, "I'm A Woman"

Sirani Avedis, for her song, "Tall Enough To Stand"

Mary Ann Lederer, for her cartoon

Rebecca Alpern, for her photograph

Connie J. Gill, for her book design and artwork.

Preface

Yvonne Duffy and I met in a rainstorm, introduced ourselves, raced to shelter, changed clothes, and found ourselves in embrace all in less than an hour. While neither of us had any idea what was coming our way, I sensed Yvonne's unique drive and vibrant air immediately. In the ensuing course of events I was to discover that Miss Duffy not only could kiss, she had a B.A. from the University of Michigan, was a property manager and was "*maybe*" going to write a book on sexuality and the disabled.

I knew she would write the book and it would be a success.

Two years later: papers are pseudo-neatly stacked according to the most absurd categories. Yvonne is hollering for some "**White-out**" while I type a request for permission to include some quotes in the book. Theresa sits by the nearest available lamp at 8:00 a.m. typing madly so Yvonne can finish the re-writes and meet the deadline for the typesetter. Kaleidoscope cross sections of personalities parade in, around, and out of the living room sorting, stamping, stapling, sticking and addressing promo fliers. Now Yvonne is taking time out for a refreshing feud with an unhappy tenant. "**More White-out!**"

The book is now complete, and I call it a success. It's informative, controversial, and, above all, **good reading.**

I knew she couldn't go wrong with lips like those. — J.

1   In the Beginning...
(Introduction)

This book was conceived in the summer of 1976, near the end of a long but stormy love relationship with a fellow writer who remarked casually one night as he was going out to see another woman, "*You think and talk so much about your sexuality as a disabled woman you ought to write about it.*"

Although I didn't think much about it then, I found myself a few days later at the University of Michigan's Graduate Library checking the card catalog to see what had been written on the sexuality of disabled women. Beyond a few articles in various professional journals dealing primarily with the child-bearing abilities of women with spinal cord injuries, there was virtually nothing. So, there was, in fact, a need for such a book.

I began to get excited. But could I write such a book? A B.A. in English certainly didn't qualify me as an expert in any of the related helping professions, and even though I am severely disabled as a result of polio which occurred when I was two years old, my experiences are still those of one individual and, as such, are limited.

I decided at the outset that this would not be a scientific study. Since there were almost no published references, nor did I have the means to accurately isolate a representative population to study. I would, therefore, use my skllls as a fiction writer to give an impressionistic sketch of what a group of disabled women were thinking and experiencing at a given space in time. I would further limit my sample to orthopedically disabled women, not because I do not think the problems and prejudices faced by visually or hearing impaired women in the development of their sexuality are not just as crucial to be aired, but because they are different they shoud, I felt, be addressed by a writer who has experienced them.

Another major concern centered around terms. Both as a writer and as a woman with specific obvious characteristics delineating her as different, I knew that there are values and connotations attached to words which extend far beyond their dictionary definitions; this is particularly true of those used to describe minorities. I wanted, therefore, to find terms possessing the most positive, optimistic connotations possible to describe this special group of women. After pondering most of the standard labels such as "physically handicapped," "physically impaired," etc., I had almost given up hope of finding just the right term until just before I began writing, it was handed to me at the Michigan Women's Music Festival in Hesperia, Michigan! All of the Festival literature sponsored by the "We Want the Music Collective," used the words, "differently abled," to designate our minority within a minority.

Differently Abled! What a wonderful phrase to describe those of us who, because of physical limitations, have learned so many other ways of carrying out everyday activities! While I would like to see *"Differently Abled"* catch on universally to denote all persons with physical limitations, male and female, I feel that it is particularly apt for use in a book about the sexual potential of group members who have made adaptations, not only to fulfill their own desires and those of their partners but also to cope with family, household, and career responsibilities. To a woman who, for so long, has been denied by society any legitimacy in these areas, this is a heady term indeed, one that has changed my whole way of looking at myself. I am much indebted to the We Want the Music Collective and the Tucson, Arizona, lesbian community who originally coined it.

The Collective brochures also referred to physically challenged women. This term, too, ignited an instant flash or recognition, for, unlike top athletes who may call into use their ultimate strength only a few times each season, most of us summon up every last bit of energy many times every day to accomplish some seemingly ordinary task. I will use this term too, perhaps not interchangeably with *"Differently Abled,"* but at times when it seems more appropriate

Developing the questionnaire was a challenge. Having done

telephone interviewing for a market research company some years ago, I knew that questions must be phrased neutrally to elicit unbiased answers, but I knew very little else about questionnaires. After scanning as many as possible, talking to people, and thinking a lot, I ended up with a sixteen-page questionnaire containing 152 questions, some of which were multiple choice and some of which required short essay-type answers. Since we know that sexuality begins to develop almost at birth and permeates virtually every aspect of our lives, it seemed important to collect data in the areas of parental attitudes, sex education, cultural preferences, self-image, and child-rearing, as well as from the more obviously relevant ones of sexual functioning, homosexuality, masturbation, menstruation, birth control, and marriage.

The second phase of the study was designed for use in a personal interview situation, but I did not receive funding from any of the numerous foundations to which I applied for travel money. Nevertheless, I was able to tape a large number of these open-ended questionnaires. The seven questions were created to encourage the women to express themselves as freely as possible. Three questions elicited personal feelings about themselves and their roles in society while the others dealt with more topical issues such as the possible use of a masturbating machine by severely disabled persons confined to institutions.

To retain the precise flavor of the women's comments, I have used quotes whenever possible. Occasionally, I have regularized spelling or added internal punctuation if doing so would clarify meanings.

Although statistics will be included whenever possible for those who wish to read them, they will not be the main focus of this book, partly, again, because of my lack of professional expertise, but also because of personal prejudice against too much numerical data. Too often, I have laid aside what may have been an otherwise interesting book when I became too bogged down with figures that seemed to have little or nothing to do with human beings. I would not like my book to suffer such a fate.

To find the women, I wrote letters to the editors of all the periodicals I could find that might be read by the Differently Abled, informing them of my intentions and requesting volunteers. With the exception of one editor who informed me that he was so inundated by such requests that he could include mine only in a paid ad, all were extremely cooperative. I received letters from ninety women, seventy-five of whom answered the first questionnaire. Thirty-nine of these also responded to the additional verbal questionnaire.

To give a more complete picture of lesbianism, two respondents, Jane and Ruth, were added later, resulting from the distribution of twenty-one revised questionnaires at the first Disabled Lesbian Conference held in August, 1981. Although the questionnaires elicited the same general information, the sections on sexual intercourse, marriage, childbirth and childrearing were eliminated, and a few of the remaining questions were reworded to reflect a more androgynous perspective. Some essay-type questions relating specifically to lesbian issues were added to the follow-up portion of the questionnaire.

So that all the women could feel free to be as open and honest as they wished without fear of embarrassment should mates, family, or friends read the book, they were assured of complete anonymity. At the top of each questionnaire was a space for the fictitious name chosen by each woman, and attached to the back of it was a separate strip of paper for the woman's real name and address. This strip was seen only by me and was immediately removed upon receipt of the completed questionnaire. Upon removal of the key slip, each woman was, henceforth, identified only by her fictitious name and her state of residence, which I decided to retain because of any possible regional differences that may be found in the responses. I retained the address slips only to forward the second part of the questionnaire and to notify participants of the book's publication.

With the exception of two women who elected to use their own names, I selected aliases for respondents who failed to indicate those they wished to use. I extend an apology to anyone displeased with a name I have chosen, but, since I consider privacy of paramount importance in a study of this nature, I had little choice.

This sample cannot be considered a barometer of what all Differently Abled women are thinking. The very fact that all have volunteered indicates an openness to discuss intimate aspects of their sexuality, a characteristic probably not representative of the entire Differently Abled female population. Furthermore, Differently Abled women in institutions are not represented. Of the several inquiries addressed to nursing homes, I received only one reply, scrawled on the bottom of my letter, stating that this institution's patients were **"not interested in sex."** Another group underrepresented is that of my Black sisters, of whom there are only two in the group. It has only been in recent years that I have seen any Black Differently Abled persons at regional meetings and conferences, but even now there are so very few Black women that I am concerned lest a triple stigma may be keeping them unnecessarily out of the mainstream.

Nor is it meant to be an objective study. By its very nature, sexuality is a subjective experience; it is what each woman says it is for her. Even such veteran sex researchers as William and Virginia Masters and Shere Hite admit that it is nearly impossible to do pure objective research on such a personal subject.

At the time of their response, (1978), only five participants were unemployed. Obviously, this is not representative of the total female Differently Abled population, for in 1970, fewer than twenty-five percent of Differently Abled women considered able to work were actually employed (1970 census figures). In view of the worsening economic situation for minorities, it is unlikely that this ratio has improved appreciably.

The largest occupational group (25) represented was that of homemaker, a status still considered by some to be unemployed, but for any woman, particularly a physically challenged woman, it is probably overemployment if the myriad of activities connected with the position are performed conscientiously. A significant number of these homemakers (17) were juggling either a career or a postsecondary education along with their multi-faceted domestic roles, again a feat considered difficult, to say the least, by most able-bodied women I have talked with who are doing it.

The next largest occupational group represented was that of college student (14), with respondents pursuing such diverse programs as Slavic languages and literature, business, and educational psychology, to name a few.

Professions accounted for a great many of the occupations. There were eight teachers; four social workers; three editors; three artists; two occupational therapists; two vocational rehabilitation counselors; one nurse; one freelance writer; one lawyer; one psychologist; one counselor; one indexer-translator; one psychological examiner; one art therapist; and one special consultant. Two women were actively involved as advocates for the Differently Abled; another read for the blind. Other participants holding positions that may be considered by some to be unusual for the Differently Abled included a dog breeder, a department store owner, and a piano teacher.

The geographical spread of respondents was fairly wide. They hailed from twenty-seven states, with the largest numbers coming from California (14) and Michigan (10). A doctor friend in Atlanta, Georgia, had predicted few, if any, respondents from the South because, *"women from the Bible Belt would be reluctant to talk about their sexuality,"* (personal correspondence) but nine showed no such temerity; of these, four were from Florida and one each from Alabama, Arkansas, Georgia, Kentucky, and Missouri. Three women lived in Canada. The others ranged from Massachusetts to Washington State.

The youngest respondent was nineteen years old, and the oldest, fifty-eight. The largest number (21) were in the 30-34-year range, with the average age being thirty-two. There were thirty-eight single women; twenty-four married; nine divorced; one separated; and three widowed. Among them, they had forty-two children. The largest family contained four children, but of the women who bore children, most had only two.

The important point of this book is that it is about women with significant Differently Abling conditions. By significant, I mean those which are severe enough to hamper a woman in carrying out her daily activities, are visible, and are likely to evoke certain biased attitudes in others.

When writing magazine editors to request participants, I stressed my desire to hear from women with all types of orthopedic disabilities for three reasons. First, I knew that a book on sexuality and the spinal cord injured woman was already in progress. Second, since the effects of spinal cord injury are more predictable and, hence, easier to measure, they have been and are likely to be studied to a far greater extent. Also, the problems encountered in the area of sexuality by women who have no sensation are often different than those who do. I was pleased that women possessing nineteen different types of disabilities responded. The largest number (20) had poliomyelitis; followed by spinal cord injury (18). The others were spread fairly evenly across the spectrum of orthopedic disabilities from arthrogryposis congenita (2) to Werdnig-Hoffman syndrome (2). A majority of women (59) used wheelchairs regularly; one women, because of the changing nature of her disease, used one from time to time; the rest were semi-ambulatory.

A profile of the average respondent, then, (if any of these unique women could be called average) would look like this: from either California or the Midwest, she is about thirty-two years old, single, well educated, either possessing a college degree or in the process of obtaining one. She is likely to have contracted polio prior to adolescence resulting in paralysis severe enough that she must use a wheelchair regularly. She is intelligent, ambitious, and forthright in speaking out on social issues. Her major concerns center around the extension of civil rights for all Differently Abled persons, with a particular emphasis on changing the attitudes of the general public which hamper her growth both as a woman and as a sexual being. She not only talks openly about these concerns but is actively involved in bringing about the needed changes.

In the following pages, I will explore the ideas and opinions of these exciting women, primarily in the area of sexuality. However, since it is not possible to isolate sexuality from the rest of our lives, you will probably end up feeling, as I have, that you know many of them as intimately as some of your closest friends.

2

A Monthly Reassurance
(Menstruation)

In most cultures, the start of menstruation is seen as the coming of age, an outward sign of puberty, of having crossed the symbolic barrier between girlhood and womanhood. Although Americans do not celebrate with tribal ceremonies, it is still a special time—often a time of particular closeness between mother and daughter. However, because of our repressive and often convoluted attitudes toward sexuality, menstruation is not always a joyful passing from girlhood into womanhood but may be more like an impressing of the female stigma upon the daughter by the mother—"the curse" supposedly visited upon us through Eve.

This stage can be even more significant for Differently Abled women. Many parents do not perceive their Differently Abled offspring as ever growing up sufficiently to function independently, and, because of this, wish to keep them forever as children. A study of sixty-three British adolescents with spina bifida (Dorner, 1977) revealed that a number of mothers were surprised that their daughters menstruated and had apparently misinformed them of the facts about it.

For parents who are unable to acknowledge their children as separate sexual beings, the onset of menstruation is particularly distressing. It is an undeniable sign of maturation, and their negative reactions cannot help but be conveyed to their children. Summer, a twenty-three-year-old college student from Illinois, described her experience this way: "*My father used to help me go to the bathroom until I got my period. He picked me up, and there was blood all over the seat of my wheelchair. Because I was only nine, he became hysterical and immediately called our family doctor to see if somehow this unnecessary hassle could somehow be detained because I wouldn't be needing it for a long time, if at all. This was not a very reinforcing action to take, and I remember it made me very skeptical about menstruation."*

Although Summer's early onset of menses was unusual, the pessimism she sensed was mentioned by eighteen others. A woman from Nevada, who called herself Poodle Gal because she is a dog breeder, said that her parents and teachers at the special school she attended *"acted as though sex and normal body functions were 'dirty'. My friends and I were thrilled when our periods finally did arrive."*

For Differently Abled women, it is even more important that the first experiences with menstruation be positive, constructive ones. To a teenager who has come to perceive her body as useless, deformed, or at best different from those of her peers, it is a wonderful affirmation of equality when her period starts at about the same time as theirs, which is usually the case. Furthermore, from then on, we receive monthly reassurance that our bodies are operating normally in an area of particular significance to us since it confirms for us our identity as sexual beings. This can be a real bulwark against society's relentless indoctrination of us as asexual. Larkin, who contracted polio when she was two years old, expressed my sentiments: *"Actually, I kind of enjoy the time of my period (although that may be a rather unfeminist thing to say)—I like to feel my body functioning."* I agree, having often marvelled that something regarded as the "curse" by so many women through the ages could make me feel so good about myself.

Fortunately, many of the first experiences with menstruation were wholesome. Thirty-eight women felt the attitudes of those presenting the information were positive. Helen W., an occupational therapist from California who encountered polio at age two, recounted, *"My mom primarily showed me what to do with sanitary pads and belts. Later, friends and I discussed all our trials and errors about learning to use Tampax. I remember one time asking my mom to help me with Tampax but ended up laughing so hard—she told me to just keep practicing, and I would get it. Eventually I did."*

In answer to the question, *"Did you know about menstruation before it occurred?"* an overwhelming majority (63) replied *"yes"*. This would seem to indicate that we are probably as well informed as our able-bodied sisters on bodily functions not directly associated with sexuality by our parents or guardians. Of those who gave the sources of their information, parents were cited most often by far (60); followed by books and pamphlets (43); friends (32); teachers (20); advertisements for sanitary products in magazines (17); siblings (9); special programs or films given in elementary school (8); nurses (3); and one doctor. Obviously, many (58) named more than one source.

Ten women did not know about menstruation before it began. Penny S. from Canada commented, "*I thought I was bleeding to death.*" It was interesting to note that Penny and six others of these were already disabled well before the age that menstruation is likely to occur. Although Penny received her elementary education in an integrated setting, five received theirs through some type of special education system. Three out of these five were educated through home teaching, (a system seldom used now and probably illegal) whereby a teacher comes for a few hours each week to the student's home to give assignments and correct those completed. I was fortunate to have learned about menstruation before it occurred from my peers and my mother, for, having had home teaching from kindergarten through the ninth grade, I can attest that the closest my teacher ever got to anything resembling biology was giving me someone's notes on the potato bug when science was required in the ninth grade.

Thirty-nine women had no particular problems associated with menstruation. Two did not reply to the question, one because she had already passed menopause and the other because she had undergone a hysterectomy at the age of twenty-three.

Of the thirty-four women indicating that they did have problems with menstruation, twenty-six described symptoms, collectively known as the Pre-Menstrual Syndrome (PMS) such as depression, tension, and fatigue as well as those of a more physical nature, cramps, headaches and water retention, which are, to varying degrees, common to most women. Eleven women suffered excessively heavy flows and frequently irregular periods, but for many of these, hormone therapy or birth control polls alleviated the problems. An exception, Mary Jones said that following her spinal cord injury her periods became increasingly irregular and stopped entirely after about a year, but in my sample, at least, this seemed unusual. Linda, a paraplegic, commented that "*despite not having sensation, I feel menstrual cramps at times,*" but she was the only spinal cord injured woman who mentioned this phenomenon.

Although water retention at the onset of menstruation is common to most women, it is often much more troublesome for Differently Abled women. Swelling in the genital area resulting from water retention was thought by some to be the cause of catheters leaking and becoming blocked more frequently. Penny S. mentioned the problem of finding an accessible bathroom at that time, for "*when I am tired, I cannot walk at all, and when I'm on my period I have to go to the bathroom more than usual.*" My personal problem, shared by a few others, is frequent bladder accidents at that time because of having to urinate more frequently than I am able to schedule attendants to help me.

Fatigue, too, although never very pleasant, is a greater problem to women who are already taxing their strength and endurance to the limits.

A few specific difficulties mentioned by my respondents appeared to be related to their particular physical condition. Jane K., a teacher from Indiana, who is a paraplegic, noticed that she is "*much more spastic shortly before and during my period.*" Yvonne Winters, also a teacher, stated, "*I am, according to the medical profession, a Twiness Syndrome which means that my chromosomes are not formed in the regular pattern. This means that the only way I could have a menstrual period was with birth control pills.*"

Answers to preferences for menstrual products were almost evenly divided between tampons (36) and pads (32), with several women using both during times of their heaviest flows. Either not being able to feel when pads or tampons need changing or the inability to change them frequently enough caused difficulties for which some good solutions were shared. For Ursula, "*hospital size napkins work best.*" Mary L. used "*two sanitary napkins with washcloth in between for menstural flow*" and added extra "*padding for any urinary incontinence*" which is more likely to occur then.

Personally, if I'm going to be away from home for any length of time around the onset of my period when there is more frequent need to urinate, I use disposable diapers in the toddler size. The cheapest variety, usually sold in plastic bags at grocery stores, work best because they are flat rectangles. More economical and more absorbent than the regular incontinence pads, the sticky tapes on the sides can be used to fasten them to the inside of your underpants or slip.

Mae Evans, a homemaker in California, who is a paraplegic, said, *"I can't feel what's going on so I must remember to change pads by the clock time."* Connie L., an unemployed thirty-year-old woman from Connecticut, found that napkins attached inside special sanitary panties with a waterproof crotch are *"more reliable and comfortable than a belt. I simply fasten the napkins to the locks on the panties while I'm sitting on the toilet, and then pull the pants up."* Liz Williams, also from Connecticut, a wheelchair user because of cerebral palsy, also preferred sanitary pants but added, *"My disappointment is that I can't find an adequate position for inserting tampons—any brand. I do have a muscle tightness problem too."*

A number of women mentioned the brand of tampons they found easiest to insert as well as the best positions for insertion. Rebecca Burns, is, I think, a very open-minded lady for she switched to tampons at the age of forty-four. She found *"Tampax and Kotex stick tampons easiest to insert, first lubricating with K-Y Jelly—manage this without help, also changing Kotex, on the toilet. This had helped my self-image."*

I recall the day my cousin, then a nursing student, inserted a tampon into me for the first time, my self-esteem rose several notches. I had never had much success with keeping pads securely where I needed them; at best, they leaked out the sides, but more often than not, they shifted completely out of position. So, it was a great relief not to have to be messy for several days each month. The real lift came, however, from the fact that it hurt only a little, a tremendous reassurance that I must be shaped like other people. Although the possibility that my sexual organs might be deformed or, in some way, non-functional had plagued me for some time, I had had no opportunity for the sexual experimentation that would have settled the issue. Nor had I the courage to express my fear to another person, who may have either been able to reassure me or see that I got to a gynecologist. Unfortunately, this worry is shared by many young women paralyzed from birth or an early age.

Since attendants unfamiliar with anatomy must insert them for me, I prefer Playtex tampons because the ends of their applicators are rounded. The attendant inserts it from the back while I'm lying on my left side with my legs slightly bent at the hips. Jane K., who is able to insert her own, also used this position. Summer, who lay on her back while her attendant inserted the tampon, said, *"it is easier to get them in comfortably if my legs are held in the air with my knees bent (resembling a sitting position)."* Helen B., a college junior from Oregon, found it easier to *"lean back against the wall in bed, put my feet together and knees out.*" For times when the vagina is dry, Julia, an artist and homemaker from Alabama, recommended a little K-Y Jelly or to hold one leg higher for insertion.

There are two themes concerning the medical profession to which I will probably return again and again throughout this book because they trouble me greatly.

The first is the apparent lack of concern for the overall health and safety of Differently Abled women. Connie L. said, "*...no doctor I ever went to has ever even examined my breasts or suggested I have any sort of gynecological examination.*"

Another example of this can be seen in the prescribing of certain drugs, either without adequate physical examination or without sufficient attention to contraindications which may be intensified by certain disabilities. Particularly risky are injections of Depo-Provera, a derivative of progesterone, used to inhibit menstruation in Differently Abled women, when we, or more likely our caretakers, decide that it is too troublesome to deal with. In much the same way as birth control pills, with most of the same side effects, it prevents ovulation. The section on Depo-Provera in the *1980 Physician's Desk Reference* (1980, p. 176) contains five references to thrombotic disorders, such as blood clots or embolisms, that may occur in patients taking this drug. Two studies (Vessey and Doll, 1969; and Sartwell et al., 1968) cited said that "*users are several times as likely to undergo thromboembolic disease without evident cause as non-users.*" This fact alone should deter physicians from prescribing it for women in wheelchairs who, because of a lack of physical activity, are apt to be more prone to circulatory problems, hence, already running a higher risk of blood clots. As though this weren't serious enough, the *Reference* warns doctors to be on the lookout for any loss of vision, migraine, signs of impaired liver function, or psychic depression. Furthermore, it is admitted that little is now known about the long range effects of prolonged use of Depo-Provera on ovarian or uterine functions. When one realizes that these facts have been disseminated by the pharmaceutical manufacturer of the drug, who obviously wishes to sell it, they are even more alarming, for one may asume that we are given the best possible picture. The actual incidence of side effects could be much higher.

In view of the above evidence, I was particularly disappointed that Sol Gordon, (Buscaglia, 1975, p. 351), prominent advocate of sex for the mentally retarded, suggested injections of Depo-Provera as birth control for those of us who cannot manage it for ourselves.

Furthermore, he did not mention any dangerous side effects.

Although the women of my acquaintance who have taken Depo-Provera (one respondent, her sister, and a former roommate) did state that their decision to do so was voluntary, it is doubtful that they were fully informed of all the possible complications. Carol Sea, a thirty-three-year-old Canadian social worker, said that both she and her sister began taking the drug when their bodies were still maturing and, so far, have had few side effects; still she worried about the unknown long-range effects. My roommate, and Carol's friend, suffered severe depression.

Therefore, I maintain that, until the medical profession, as a whole, regards our bodies to be as valuable as we do, **we** must be responsible for our own health safety. By this, I mean that we must independently research the drugs prescribed for us by our doctors, whenever possible, **before** we begin taking them. The most recent **Physician's Desk Reference**, available at most libraries or fairly inexpensive to purchase, is a good source of basic facts and is quite readable with the aid of a medical dictionary. Then, as informed consumers, we can discuss the advantages versus disadvantages of the drugs with the doctor and, together, decide on its use for us.

My second concern is the remarkable disinterest of the rehabilitation profession in providing us with the kind of specific information related to our particular disabilities, information that would relieve our minds of anxiety and enable us to live more freely as full sexual beings. Connie L., who has amyotonia congenita, said, "*I can't seem to manage them (tampons) and still wonder if it's simply a matter of dexterity (or lack thereof) or if there's some vaginal malformation...I have no particular reason for thinking that except that the combination of the disability and the general disregard of my sexuality tend to make me feel as if something must be wrong.*" Linda, a housewife who became a paraplegic at the age of seventeen, said, "*it was about a year after my injury before I tried using Tampax instead of pads. I had always used Tampax previously, but was afraid of hurting myself because of the catheter and not being able to feel if it was inserted properly.*" These are specific instances of situations in which some information and support could have lessened worry. There are some notable exceptions, however, such as the doctor of Easy Goer, a rehabilitation counselor from New Jersey, who, she said, "*was extremely helpful in suggesting the use of tampons.*" But all too often, Jane K's experience, "*The rehab. people seemed to know nothing about female hygiene or the special menstrual problems that sometimes do occur,*" is much more typical.

In the area of menstruation, as in the other areas of sexuality covered in this book, my respondents have proved to be remarkably normal in most ways, despite the strange attitudes often presented by parents or guardians and the lack of supportive assistance from medical and rehabilitation personnel. Those problems we have encountered have involved managing the hygiene of it. Through the ingenuity of our respondents, however, most of these difficulties have been resolved; and, overall, we have managed to maintain a healthy perspective on this facet of our sexuality.

3

Fact or Fiction?
Ignorance Can Hurt
(Sex Education)

Sex education in general has been a hot issue in the U.S. over the past decade or so. As our interest with sex, fanned by the media, has mushroomed into a major controversy, so has our desire to know as much as possible about it. Books on sex purporting to fill in the gaps of our misinformation such as *Everything You Always Wanted to Know About...The Joy Of...The Sensuous...*, ad infinitum, whether or not they are accurate, have become immediate bestsellers. Porno shops have been moving into more middle class neighborhoods, and, except for occasional citizens' skirmishes, have been flourishing. Ads for love potions, vibrators and other sexual aids are making their way into the better magazines.

The biggest controversy, however, has centered around sex education in the schools. Is it usurping the prerogative of parents? Who is qualified to teach it? What shall be taught? Which materials should be used? Can or should the curriculum be reconciled with the various religious views of the students attending the classes? These issues are still being studied, discussed, and fought over in school districts and even courts around the country; meanwhile, young people seem to be learning about sex in about the same ways they always have—a little here, a little there, then, piecing the bits of knowledge together to form a reasonably accurate, if limited, whole.

As one might expect, friends were by far the most frequently mentioned sources of information on sex (55) with books following close behind (52). Parents, too, were important sources (41). Twenty-four women each received most of their sex information from siblings or school classes. Six learned the basics from watching animals. Jay Kirfirst, a part-time piano teacher from Indiana said, "*I learned about sex mostly from conversations I wasn't to hear and later from magazines and books.*" Two others also learned from overhearing.

Sol Gordon (1974) points out that because the disabled are kept so ignorant of sexual expression we are much more likely to be exposed to sexual exploitation. This is exactly what happened to two of my respondents. Penny S. recounted, "*At the age of fifteen, I was still very naive—a man about forty-five told me about the sexual act over the phone.*" Charlene, an unemployed hemiplegic from Michigan learned firsthand from an "*elderly man who tried to rape me at eleven years; then, my father sat down and explained it to me.*"

When asked if this first information they received was accurate, forty-two women said most of it was, nineteen said all of it, and ten said that only some of it was correct. Raising the possibility that friends, parents, siblings, or even books may not be the best sources of information were Dahtee, a speech teacher from Massachusetts, who said that none of what she learned was correct and cited her first lover as her most reliable teacher, and Brillig, a forty-seven-year-old editor from Michigan who didn't get her misinformation completely straightened out until she took a biology course in college.

Although the majority of women felt that the information they did receive was largely accurate, thirteen found it inadequate and irrelevant to their specific physical conditions. Connie L. said that her "*formal education was lacking in practically everything. As I read more and more, the mechanical and even some of the psychological elements were filled in, but what I didn't know was how I fit in. I never received any help from anyone, including doctors, in coming to terms with my own sexuality. The silence, I suppose, said it all....From my parents and most of my relations, I got the general impression that I was assumed to be asexual. Friends are a bit more help. Friends do not so much make suggestions as present a more encouraging attitude.*" Linda commented, "*What I wanted to know was whether I could be a satisfactory mate.*"

Ten women wanted to know more about the emotional aspects of sex. Owen, a Michigan college student who became paralyzed when she was eighteen, said, "*Emphasis should have been placed on 'feelings' instead of mechanics.*" Agreeing was Hot Wheels, a student from Florida, who found "*lacking were any explanation of feelings with orgasms, intercourse. It was straight mechanics and 'love'. No birth control was mentioned.*" Five others noted tha lack of birth control information. Four women felt that a more positive attitude toward sex was needed.

Four others wished for the basic facts of intercourse. Jennifer, a homemaker-salesperson whose myasthenia gravis began at age fifteen, felt there was "*need for more one-to-one talks, movies, frank discussions, more on babies and actual birth.*" Of the films shown in fifth, sixth and eighth grades at her school, Larkin's criticisms were, "*Much was lacking—no mention of touching, fun, masturbation, fucking, pregnancy, etc.,—I think* [they] *were basically an ad for Kotex.*" Three women felt that the societal aspects of sex were missing from their education. One each wanted to know more about female anatomy and functioning as well as homosexuality.

With the exception of Larkin, who, although she contracted polio at the age of two years, was, nevertheless, educated in a completely integrated setting, these quotes came from women who, at the time of acquiring their basic sex education, were able-bodied, were students in standard public school systems, and received it in the usual ways. That they found so much lacking is not surprising because, even with all the hubbub, most Americans still find it difficult to discuss sex in any kind of healthy, realistic way.

If sex education in a so-called "normal" school system is so unsatisfactory, what will be the experience of women Differently Abled from birth or an early age who have received their general education by means of some special system? Rebecca Burns, a forty-eight-year-old Californian who had home teaching, "*was twelve before I understood that intercourse is pleasurable.*" Mary James related, "*...when a boy with quite severe cerebral palsy told me to feel him through his pants, I thought he was nuts and if another made a comment about my breasts, I thought he was a pervert. And when yet another wanted to kiss me in high school, and made sexual gestures, I thought I had to love him very much before I even relaxed and enjoyed the moment for itself.*"

It is very clear from these comments and others that the lively interest in sex education mentioned earlier has never reached the ears of administrators responsible for the special education systems in which my respondents were students. We are still as sexless as ever in the eyes of everyone significantly connected with us during our growing up years—parents, teachers, and rehabilitation personnel.

In response to the question about whether anyone had attempted to relate the women's sex education to their specific physical situation, fifteen replied that the person giving the information had either told them or implied that sex would be impossible. Summer, who has amyotonia congenita, said, **"When I was in special ed., we had no sex education, and we were not invited when the rest of the school had movies,"** and she went on to advise, **"I think sex education should also include a lesson that sex is for everyone. When I heard about sex, I did not see myself as being able to take an active part."** Poodle Gal, whose spinal muscular atrophy began at the age of fifteen months, related an almost identical experience, **"All elements were lacking as we were made to feel that since we were handicapped, sex and anything close to it was not for us. No one even wanted us at school to know or even think about sexual maturity."** Annette, a secretary at a famous rehabilitation facility in Georgia, felt that **"implications always seemed to be made by family and friends that sex and marriage would not be part of my life."**

Even worse than no information at all was the misinformation some of us received, often from those closest to us. Sandy Mitchell, a twenty-five-year-old assistant editor from New York whose muscular dystrophy began at age twelve, remembered, **"The doctor who diagnosed me...said I shouldn't date or marry (no sex was implied, but I was too young to realize that). This, I'm sure, influenced my parents who never mentioned sex to me."** April, who contracted polio at the age of two, said, **"My mother told me not to even think about marriage, sex, etc., because I wouldn't be able to participate—she had no medical basis for her opinion and was wrong, of course."** Anet's expierence was similar: **"Mother told me I might be sterile because of numerous pelvic x-rays during childhood."** Marlene C., whose polio occurred at the age of seven said, **"As a child and teenager, I learned from family and peers that I had no sexuality only sexual feelings which I should suppress. Within the past eight or ten years, I have gotten information allowing me to recognize my own sexuality and to receive specific information from other disabled people, professionals in psychology and sexual adjustment of disabled."**

Twenty-one women said that no attempt whatever had been made to relate sexual information to their particular condition. Mrs. Lewis, a fifty-three-year-old retired teacher who contracted polio at the age of twenty-five, said that when she was being rehabilitated, *"sex was **never**, but never talked about. Only: 'Don't get pregnant; you're a cripple now', said by a doctor."* Brillig, a mother of four, said, *"After I had polio* [age twenty], *I was told I would have to have any childen by Caesarian section (didn't)."* Referring to intercourse, she continued, *"My P.T. wondered what I'd do about my back brace. (I take it off)."*

Although it is true that twenty-five or thirty years ago everyone was more reticent about discussing sex, the experiences of my respondents show that in rehabilitation circles, unfortunately, little has changed. Jane K., who became paralyzed about four years ago, said, *"Sex was never mentioned by rehab. people. Under pressure, they still would not discuss it with me—a female."* Julia, a twenty-five-year-old Alabama artist said, *"Over a period of six years, maybe one or two of my doctors told me I would be able to have sex, but they didn't know if I would enjoy it. They said I would only have the satisfaction of pleasing my mate."* We could rationalize here that Indiana and Alabama may not be very progressive states in the area of rehabilitation if we didn't have the following incisive report from Mae Evans, a California homemaker who became a paraplegic at the age of forty-six. *"I rehabilitated at a **major** university hospital considered in the U.S. top seven for medical school graduate training...My sex feelings were wiped out with the paraplegia, and I was scared—after twenty years of good sex, what was I to do? Not one time did a doctor or therapist or nurse try to draw me out on this. Two times I attempted to express my fears but was rejected with (1) 'Your vagina is the same as before—it won't hurt it to have intercourse. But remember you can still get pregnant,' and (2) 'Forget about sex—there are other things.' I figured if these experts felt this way, there must be something wrong with **me** so I shut up. Once home I avoided sex for a whole year (my poor husband!) Then I went to a psychiatrist—not to talk about sex, but I found out I **was** talking about it. He saw the problem and need, drew me out, and gave me the courage to face the situation. He said, 'In all my dealings with rehabilitation people, the two things they always overlook are depression and sex counseling.' That was sure true in my case!"* Hot Wheels summed it up, *"All in all, I feel that my sexual education was lacking. I feel that especially since I am disabled, something should be said about methods, problems, etc. I've managed, but it could have been better with info."* Linda, mother of a five-year-old son, said, *"After my injury, I was told I could still have children. More emphasis*

31

was placed on the difficulty of taking care of them. I had little detail on intercourse."

Unfortunately, she went on to say, *"but I didn't ask the right questions."* The self-blame I detect in this statement is so unnecessary. You, first, have to know something about a subject in order to assess what you don't know and to be able to ask the questions that will fill in the gaps. It may be argued that at seventeen years old—the age at which Linda was injured—she could be expected to know something about sex. However, at the time of a traumatic accident or illness there is so much that is fearful, unknown, or misunderstood about this experience, which may necessitate a radical alteration of lifestyle that I don't think one should also be expected to know enough about the factors of this new situation to ask *"the right questions"* about sex. Since rehabilitation professionals are in the key positions to see the overall picture, it should be their responsibiity to study the implications of the traumatizing factor, relate it to what is already known about human sexuality, and, while always keeping in mind the unknown potential of each individual, convey their findings to the client in language she understands.

Infomation about sex is usually acquired by able-bodied children in bits and pieces from brothers and sisters, friends, parents, and sometimes through sex education classes. For those of us who have had a traumatizing accident or illness at birth or an early age, these natural progressions are interrupted or may never even occur. Cerebral palsy being congenital, Liz Williams, a thirty-one-year-old data transcriber who received her elementary education in a special classroom that was part of a rehabilitation center, said, *"Because of my innocence of being a kid, I never questioned, or thought, then, that there may be problems, or that sex and marriage may not happen to me."* Again, I question that we would have enough general information on sex to anticipate the types of problems that might arise in order to ask the *"right questions."* Looking back, I doubt that I would have been able to phrase to a professional the correct questions to elicit the reassurance I so desperately needed about my body's ability to function sexually. Even had I known exactly what I wanted to know, I probably would have been too shy to ask. Therefore, to be given some background sexual information geared to our age and experiential levels as well as to our specific physical abilities would be beneficial in helping to forestall the kinds of problems which grow from ignorance and, all too often, rob us of our innate good feelings about ourselves as sexual beings.

The following—a beautiful exception to the general apathy about

Female Sex Organs

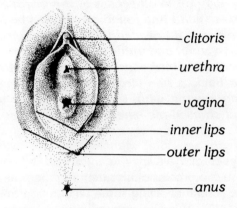

clitoris
urethra
vagina
inner lips
outer lips
anus

Male Sex Organs

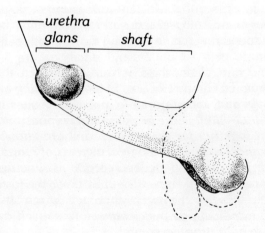

urethra
glans
shaft

sex education for the Differently Abled—illustrates the real difference that can be made with only a little concern and effort. Deena's reaction to the doctor showing her the inside of her vagina when she was twenty-nine was, "**Boy, was that a shock! It was a good feeling to know I was a woman in all senses of the word. He also showed me my clitoris which I had found on my own before by feel; now I knew where it was if I needed to help my boyfriend. I was also shown my birth canal and made aware that there was no reason why I could not have intercourse. When I went back for another visit, I came back a non-virgin, thanks to a very gentle and understanding doctor who took his time to answer all my questions and showed me where everything was.**"

Although, seven of the twelve women who did obtain relevant information from the professionals attending them did receive it from doctors, there is now evolving some recognition that sex education of the Differently Abled, particularly in reference to a specific physical characteristic, might be carried out more effectively through a team approach. This does not absolve doctors of their responsibility to the patient in this area, however, but there are several reasons why the relaying of this relevant information might be better accomplished by others on the rehabilitation team. Despite their active acquaintance with the most intimate parts of our anatomy, doctors are already known to be lacking in actual sexual knowledge. Furthermore, since doctors usually only see patients for a few minutes a day while we are hospitalized and much less frequently once we return to our homes, there is little opportunity for the development of the kind of intimacy that facilitates discussion of sexual concerns. On the other hand, nurses and various therapists, because they traditionally spend much time working directly with patients are in a much better position to understand what we are feeling about ourselves and our relationships as well as our actual abilities and potential. Scout L. Gunn (1977, p. 5) feels "**Hearing and responding to feelings and, when possible, answering questions regarding sexual functioning is the professional responsibility of people who 'have it together for themselves' and are knowledgeable in the physiological and psychological aspects of human sexuality. They could just as well be recreators as doctors or social workers.**" Kolodny et al. (pp. 257-258) favor the fostering of our sexual health through the team approach which would include "**clergy and handicapped peer counselors as well as the whole gamut of rehabilitation personnel.**"

A step in the right direction was reported by Neistadt and Baker in the **American Journal of Occupational Therapy** (1978, pp. 646-647). Operating on the premise that sex is part of daily living, the occupational therapy staff of Massachusetts Rehabilitation Hospital initiated a sex counseling program. Usually introduced a week or two before the patient was expected to be discharged, the program consisted of presenting an illustrated informational booklet containing concrete suggestions for overcoming various functional problems which was followed by discussion. Of sixty-one patients counseled the first year, thirty-six felt the sessions were "*very helpful.*"

The Department of Physical Medicine and Rehabilitation at University Hospital here in Ann Arbor seems to have had a good record in addressing patients' sexuality even before the arrival, from the University of Minnesota, of Ted and Sandra Cole, pioneers in sexuality and disability. Marie R., a thirty-year-old mother of three, who became a paraplegic at the age of nineteen, was told by the doctors on this unit that she would be able to function normally as a sexual being. Owen, who rehabilitated there about three years ago, reported, "*My doctor and physical therapist discussed with me the differences I would encounter after my disability.*"

Three women reported that they were actually encouraged by their teachers and doctors to participate in sexual activity. Midge, a fifty-five-year-old community relations specialist who was four when she contracted polio, felt fortunate that her teachers at home and at a special school were "*ahead of their time.*" Kathryn, a fifty-nine-year-old Washington artist whose polio occurred when she was twenty-four, recalled, "*In the year I spent in the hospital, the doctors always reminded me the sex drive and function was not gone, and it was healthy to let sex and sexuality take a natural path. I have a lot to thank those men for.*"

The other major area felt to be lacking in their sex eduction was information about the opposite sex. Ten women said they wanted to know everything about men. Anet, a forty-one-year-old Oregon musician and reader for a blind student, "*wanted to know everything about the opposite sex, including how to make them worship me.*" Pooh Grayson, a thirty-six-year-old California counselor who is a post polio quad, agreed with Anet—"*Everything—how they function physically, their feelings and thoughts about sex in general, and me in particular.*" Michelle, who uses a wheelchair because of multiple sclerosis and is a social worker in Florida, wanted to know "*what they looked like, what sensations they have, how to succeed with.*"

Five women wanted to understand male sexuality in relation to society's norms. Sally Smith, a thirty-five-year-old Wisconsin housewife, asked, "*Do men really see females as sex symbols?*" Carol Sea, who was born with the Werdnig Hoffman Syndrome, wanted to know "*How come men/boys are more easily able to have sex with people they don't care about?*"

Nineteen women desired basic facts about male anatomy and functioning. As we already know, Differently Abled women are frequently deprived of the ordinary social contact between siblings and peers such as the childhood games of Doctor or Striptease by means of which information is usually gained during childhood and adolescence. April said, "*Because I didn't have any brothers or male contacts, I was always very curious what a penis really looked like.*" Rebecca Burns described her experience thus: "*In my forties, I first learned from reading and photographs, details of male anatomy and sexual functions. A pen pal told me (complete with polaroids of his erection) all I wanted to know. It was very helpful.*" Helen W., an occupational therapist in California who contracted polio at the age of two years, wanted to know "*just how males functioned during intercourse—the actual physiology of the male anatomy.*" Summer recalled, "*The first thing I wanted to know after I found out how sex occurred was how did the penis fit into the vagina....I also wondered what their bodies felt like—I mean just their skin and muscles, etc.*" Colette, a twenty-eight-year-old Washington housewife, who has had Fredrich's ataxia since she was five years old, was "*extremely interested in the male penis because I did not, then or now, have one.*" Sandy Mitchell wanted to know "*how a male feels (physically) when he ejaculates.*"

Nine women wished for more information about male emotions and interests. Yana DaShana, a thirty-five-year-old post-polio indexer-translator from Ohio, lacked knowledge about both "*their physical role in sex and emotional response.*" Deena was puzzled about what may be considered the eternal question, "*Why do men mean or say the total opposite of their actions?*" Jane Smith, a vocational rehabilitation counselor from Pennsylvania, "*wanted to know how to please men sexually.*" Liz Williams regretted her "*limited opportunity for developing relationships that would allow me to know a man in all ways.*" Larkin commented, "*I would like to know individual men as intimate friends,*" and wanted to know "*the same things I want to know about my women friends."* Mary James, who is single, thirty, and calls herself a professional volunteer, needed *"information on sexual arousal techniques, etc.—more on 'sexuality' than sex."*

I recently came across a book which, although it was written primarily to help men better understand themselves, is an excellent guide for women to learn more about male emotions and sexual responses. Called **Male Sexuality** by Bernie Zilbergeld, Ph.D. (New York: Little, Brown and Company, 1978), it contains lots of anecdotes and case histories, and, in my opinion, answers many of the kind of questions one can usually ask only an intimate male friend or lover. It is also helpful in suggesting numerous ways to please men sexually, most of which Differently Abled women could do.

Five women wished to understand more about male acceptance of them as Differently Abled. Jane Grant, a thirty-five-year-old divorcee and mother of three, who, at the time of her response, was a member of the Vermont Governor's committee on the Handicapped, wondered, *"why a handicap repels some men and others it doesn't at all."* Helen Beach, a twenty-six-year-old paraplegic, would like to know *"why men feel so protective of me when I am so independent? It just creates conflicts."*

I feel it is significant that eight women replied *"Nothing"* when asked what they, presently or in the past, wanted to know about the opposite sex. Had they received such complete information about the male anatomy, functioning, and psyche that there was simply nothing more they were interested in learning? Considering the paucity of sexual information mentioned by most women, this is very doubtful. More likely, they were indoctrinated by the negative attitudes of their parents and other caretakers into thinking that they could not be sexual beings. So they saw as useless the seeking of knowledge in an area from which they had already been excluded. After all, who goes around studying an architect's blueprints if one, at some time, does not plan to construct a building? Patricia Maher, a thrity-year-old student from Michigan who uses a wheelchair because of cerebral palsy, said that she *"never was interested because I believed no man would be interested."*

Another reason may be fear—fear of being inadequate, fear of the unknown, as verbalized by Colleen Moore, a mother of two and a special consultant living in California, who wanted to know *"very little—I was afraid of the opposite sex."* It saddens me to realize the extent that our sexual development has been hampered by those old bugaboos of fear and ignorance.

In spite of all the obstacles blocking our acquisition of the sexual knowledge we need to be fully developed and functioning human beings, we are still somehow expected to have it all together by the time we become adults. Jay Kirfirst expressed this myopia rather well when she stated that although she missed *"all general information that is part of growing, now everyone assumes I know it all—by myself."* Primarily through our own ingenuity, most of us have done pretty well in securing the necessary information. Mary James said, *"I don't know many things, I feel; though knew a lot of what was in **Everything You Always Wanted to Know About Sex** so maybe I know more than I thought about general aspects."*

In order to facilitate the kind of open acceptance and free discussion which will enhance the natural maturation of Differently Abled women as sexual beings, a basic change in attitudes must occur. Yvonne Winters, an Ohio teacher who has used a wheelchair for several years as a result of an unnamed neurological disorder, said, *"I really think the public in general feel that the disabled do not really have any feelings in this area—thus, much of the information they need is lacking."* Although I've heard Jennifer's complaint that *"doctors are shy about sex talk,"* voiced most often by t.a.b. women, it is more significant to us. Because we may be already cut off from the common sources of general knowledge and may have no one else to turn to for specific sexual information relating to our individual states, it is imperative that doctors lay aside their own insecurities so that, in the spirit of the good doctor mentioned on page 34, they can acquire the sensitivity to do whatever is required to treat our whole persons.

The picture is not all bleak; encouraging signs of enlightenment are occurring here and there. In the past year or two, a number of seminars on sexuality and disability have been held for doctors throughout the country, with credit in continuing medical education given for their attendance. Also positive is Helen Beach's statement: *"The Human Sexuality course I took in college made every effort to include disabled persons. Guest speakers with disabilities gave a great deal of information which may have helped change some students' negative attitudes to positive."*

There must be many more such activities as well as less formal interactions, and we must continue to push for them in whatever eductional, clinical or social spheres within which we have influence.

4

The Image Makers
(Parental Attitudes)

In this chapter, we will explore more specifically how parental attitudes about our special physical condition contribute to the formation of the self-image—positive or negative—of those of us Differently Abled at birth or an early age. To a lesser degree, they may also be instrumental in the continuance of the concept of self held prior to a traumatizing accident or illness which occurs later in life.

To better understand the reasons parents of Differently Abled offspring hold the attitudes they so frequently do, it is helpful to learn something about relationships between parents and their able-bodied children. According to Gordeuk (1976), there are many reasons why persons decide to have babies, not the least of which are narcissistic—expectations that the child will somehow reflect glory on their parents by enhancing their self-esteem, advancing their social status, achieving their unattained career goals, etc. Our society's emphasis on the perfect and the successful further serves to promote these expectations.

Once the baby has arrived, she/he and the mother must learn to like each other. Contrary to popular belief, this bond does not occur spontaneously, but, like other types of attraction results from the mutual meeting of needs. In this case, in return for keeping her infant fed, clean, dry and comfortable, the mother receives reinforcement from the baby's smiles, health, and development, the feeling of competence in meeting her/his needs, and the approval of others, etc., for meeting these needs.

For a mother who gives birth to a less-than-perfect baby, this natural process may be delayed, interrupted at some point or never fully completed. This is unpleasant to contemplate, I agree, but upon seeing her infant for the first time she may be appalled at the unanticipated appearance of the deformity. Fear is also a common emotional reaction. It may stem from the mother's fear of her own inadequacy in having produced a less-than-perfect infant, fear of her inability to provide for its special needs, society's reaction to her and/or the child, or some combination of these. Lastly, a Differently Abled baby may not be able to provide the mother with the amount or kind of positive reinforcement she needs for successful nurturing.

Whether their child is born with her/his specific physical condition or acquires it later, most parents experience a grieving process (Wright, 1976). These stages—shock, denial, guilt and anger, shame and martyrdom, depression and recovery—are similar to the grief suffered by persons losing loved ones through death, divorce, long distance moves or other abrupt emotional deprivation. In this case, the loss is the death of the dream of the perfect child. Pooh Grayson illustrated for us two parents at different points in this process: *"When I became disabled, something inside my mother died. She will never get over the shock of having a less-than-perfect child. She has remained a devoted parent however. She has provided me with the necessities, given me much moral support and is very proud of my accomplishments. My father accepted my disability as part of life and continued meeting my material needs as a responsible parent. He is proud of my accomplishments with one exception. Because of my disability, he disapproved of my having children. He did not feel a disabled person could manage without laying a burden on others."*

Shock, the initial stage, is usually a numbed disbelief when confronted by the facts of their child's physical condition. A natural reaction to pain, shock is, by its very nature, short-lived and is usually followed by denial.

Denial may be characterized by parents who *"shop around"* for a doctor who will give them the diagnosis they want (Buscaglia, 1975). My mother, sure that polio was only temporary, dragged me around to faith healers for several years before she adjusted. Colette, whose Fredrich's ataxia began when she was five years old, recalled that she *"received no special treatment, but was reared as though I would someday simply outgrow my 'clumsiness'."* Anet, who contracted polio when she was only ten days old, said, *"My father yelled at me to 'be more careful' when I fell."*

Anger and guilt arise when the unalterable facts of the child's condition can no longer be ignored; parents become angry that such a misfortune has befallen **them**. Since ancient times, physical disability has been associated with past sin. This belief persists—on a sub-conscious level, at least. Certainly, many parents are plagued with guilt over what they may have done wrong, either in their own lives or in relation to their child, to cause them to deserve such a fate. This phase is particularly difficult for the whole family, for parents frequently blame and criticize each other excessively and just generally take out their frustrations on other family members. This places a tremendous strain on the marriage bond; many dissolve at this stage, thereby triggering even more anger and guilt. It appears, however, that some outward expression of this anger is essential in order to progress to the next stages.

One of the reasons for this anger may be related to fear of not being adequate to the tremendous challenges facing them. In a little book, **And God Said 'No.'** about the early months of her daughter's polio, Lael Cappaert writes, "*...it probably was not the number of duties that kept me harried. It was the constant concern that I do everything for Andi not only to the best of my ability, but with absolute perfection. How could I ever face Andi, the young woman, if her recovery were hindered by my carelessness or neglect?*" (p. 79.)

Guilt often results because a parent resents the time spent with one child perhaps to the detriment of other children, her/himself or a spouse. Larkin noted: "*I think my mom was afraid of the responsibility, resented the time commitment, felt guilty—consequently, I feel as though Dad raised me while my mom took over with the other three kids.*"

Larkin's observations demonstrate a kind of distancing on the part of the mother which is also illustrated by Ursula. Having had Werdnig-Hoffman's syndrome since birth, she felt she "*was treated very much as an object—no expectation but wanted me to 'be happy'. Family is very damaging to my self-concept, and I stay away from them as much as possible.*"

Since a large part of the mother-daughter relationship involves initiating the daughter into the ways of womanhood, there may be a turning away because the mother does not see the daughter as being able to fulfill her version of the feminine role. This is particularly evident in the comment of Linda, a thirty-three-year-old housewife, "*My mother didn't want me to marry. She was afraid I would be hurt and not be able to hold a husband—she has been married four times...I was willing to take the chance. Even if my marriage doesn't last, I did the right thing and would be able to cope with it."* Marlene C., a post-polio who is now a psychological examiner in Arkansas, had a similar experience: *"My mother told me one time that she had a special love for me which she attributed to knowing I would never hurt her by getting pregnant before marrying as my older sister had; also that she knew I would never marry."*

Rejection can happen at any age at which a daughter becomes Differently Abled. Brillig, whose polio occurred at twenty, related this experience: *"My mother tried to kill me, tried to get me to kill myself, and tried to get me to become an alcoholic."* This extreme example symbolizes not the destruction of the person but of the relationship.

As objects of all this anger and guilt, we may be either denied the love and nurturance that is every child's birthright, or be extremely over-protected in a parental attempt to overcompensate for these negative but natural feelings. The latter is far more common. J.J., a thirty-two-year-old graduate student from New York, said, *"My siblings (three—all younger) grew up with an attitude of protectiveness toward me. I was expected to participate, but in event of breakage I was expected to get out of the way and let others deal with it."* Noted Rebecca Burns, *"They learned that my trying new things would end in my disappointment. They couldn't face the risk."* Helen W., who contracted polio when she was two years old, recalled, *"I was older than my friends before I crossed the street alone or rode my bike all over the neighborhood like they did. I had responsibilities to take care of my room and things but never had to do household chores."*

Washington artist and homemaker, Daisy D. was *"forbade to try* [household duties] *on account I might hurt myself and then be more of a burden. (I did anyway...got scolded and spanked)."* The discipline of Woodie, who was born with spina bifida and, at the time of her response, was a college junior in California, was less severe than that experienced by her siblings. *"I was hardly ever spanked, and the punishment I received when I was bad was mild compared to what my brother would get for the same thing."*

Not all parents may experience every stage or experience them in sequence: some stages may overlap. For example, shame and martyrdom, the next stage, are closely related to guilt, but while they may occur simultaneously, there are significant differences. Guilt is an internal feeling stemming from the belief that one has done something wrong. Shame is external in that it is related to one's perception of having lost respect, prestige, etc., in the eyes of others. For instance, Daisy D., who has arthrogryposis congenita, said, "*Dad was very proud of his body and ashamed people would think some 'social disease' had caused my deformities. Mom covered my hands so not to offend people.*"

Very likely, shame as well as anger and resentment, was an operational factor in the experience of Mary James, who has used a wheelchair most of her life. She said that she received "*no special treatment but never received a good self-image. Parents could always do things 'faster and better' than I could, they said, and I was 'too much trouble' to usually take places, etc.*" A teacher and apartment building manager from Kentucky, E. B. Browning, also "*was 'sheltered' for convenience's sake.*"

Martyrdom may set in as the parents relinquish more and more friendships and activities to devote themselves to the needs of their Differently Abled child, (Buscaglia, 1975, p. 123). The mother, usually the primary caretaker, as she finds herself increasingly isolated with the child, may begin to view her whole fulfillment as a woman connected to her/him and may even delay the child's progress in order to preserve her own narrowing sense of self-worth. A regular system of relief for the major caretaking parent is essential so that she/he can continue to grow as an individual.

Equally important to the recovery process are counseling and supportive services. In a two-year English study on mothers of congenitally Differently Abled babies, (Burden, 1980), the initial testing when the babies were two months old showed the mothers were severely depressed. Weekly home visits by a developmental therapist were instituted. Two years later, a comparison of these women with a control group of similar mothers who had had approximately the same severity of depression showed that, although both groups were less depressed, the mothers who had received the weekly support of the visiting therapist, exhibited a much greater improvement in their mental health. Even allowing for other relevant factors such as the mental health of parents and the stability of the marriage relationship prior to the arrival of their Differently Abled child it seems clear that education and supportive services **do** indeed make a difference, not only to the parents but also to the Differently Abled child, for, according to Dr. Buscaglia (1975, p. 77) the rest of the family will usually adopt the mother's attitude toward the child.

Since these kinds of assistance which can make a real difference are so seldom available, it is not surprising that when respondents were asked their perceptions of their parents' attitudes toward their specific physical condition, thirty-three felt that the attitudes were negative. This may not seem like a large majority until we consider that only forty-five of the women became Differently Abled before the age of fifteen years. These perceptions seem to have been based largely on how they were treated in relation to other siblings. Eight responses were designated as neutral either because they did not clearly fall to one side or the other or because there was a disparity in perceived attitudes between the two parents. The latter situation probably indicated that each parent was at a different stage of the grieving process, as in Connie L.,'s situation: "*I was over-protected. Though both parents were loving and giving, I think only my mother (who died a year ago) understood that 'being taken care of,' even loved, was not enough. My father, with the best of intentions, has a way of reinforcing my own worst fears about myself and the kind of life I can lead.*"

By not being allowed to assume responsibilities (in relation to our physical abilities) appropriate to our age level and by not being expected to achieve in any way, we are kept in a perennial state of dependence usually associated with childhood. Even though we start out in life with mental faculties equal to those of our siblings and peers, we fall behind developmentally when we are not allowed to face the same challenges as we mature. Jay Kirfirst's experience is typical: "*I knew what I could and could not do and was not spoiled, though never was I encouraged to go out to college or to work.*"

When we are not allowed to try new experiences and to learn from them, even though we may fail, we are unable to gain the feeling of self-confidence which occurs with increasing mastery of our environment. Colette was fortunate to have been able to persuade her mother that she should be allowed to try living independently: "*My mother wanted me to return to the nursing home as soon as she found out we were living together! Her words were, 'Get your clothes together at once! I'm taking you back to the nursing home this morning.' I objected, cried a little and finally got her to realize that I wasn't a child anymore.*"

Recovery is the final stage of grief. An essential component of the recovery process is acceptance—acceptance of imperfections and shortcomings in themselves, in others, and in their Differently Abled child. This seems to be a difficult step for many parents. Lola, whose polio occurred at fourteen, drew this conclusion, "*My Dad had extreme difficulty in accepting that I'd never walk—I'm not sure he ever has completely. Also, now he doesn't really accept me as a* *woman with sexual desires and needs. Example: he has said he can't see what any man would see in me.*" Expressing the mores of that period, Daisy D.'s mother "*instilled great fear of venereal disease and 'sexploitation,' promiscuity, and pregnancy, and sex without marriage.*" But her real bias is revealed as she continued, "*that no one would marry a cripple anyway so do not allow sex ever!*" (Daisy ended by reiterating what we all know.) "*This concept proved untrue—I did marry at age eighteen, pregnant at age twenty-one.*"

To sufficiently come to terms with their child as a sexual being, and to provide her/him with correct sexual information is vital, for, according to Dorner (1977), parents are the main sources of these facts for Differently Abled children. Although able-bodied children usually acquire this knowledge from peers, predictably, he found students enrolled in special education facilities far less knowledgeable about sex (pp. 230-231). Since we already know that sex education classes are rarely available to us, this responsibility ultimately becomes the parents'.

When it is either inaccurate, prejudiced or not given at all, the results can be devastating. Patricia Maher's words cannot be overemphasized: "*Parents should be made to teach and talk to their child as if* [she/he] *were a normal child. I feel handicapped people should be made to feel freer to talk about their sexuality.*" Ursula echoed my own experience in her comment, "*...it was made clear (by parents) that I should not expect to engage in sexual activity.*" This non-acceptance (or outright rejection) of something so basic to our whole personality as our sexuality can be devastating to our self-concepts whether we internalize the verdict, as all too many of us do, or whether we revolt against it, as I did when I went to bed with every man I could for about the first five years I lived away from home. No matter how many times they're proved wrong, there is always that nagging doubt, that somehow they must know some truth about us that we don't—the infallibility of parents remains a powerful myth. The anger resulting from their cruel and needless amputation of a portion of our humanness further cramps our own emotional growth and/or is transferred to others.

Fortunately, some parents do make the transition into recovery which, according to Gordeuk (op. cit.), involves two other steps, reconstruction and reorientation. Reorientation, in this case, means extending themselves beyond their own unique situation into the community to work with other parents of Differently Abled children to increase educational opportunities, lobby for legislation, etc. For our purposes, however, we are mainly interested in how well they are able to reconstruct their lives around the adaptations for the Differently Abled child so that the whole family can live and grow normally without guilt or shame.

Families do recover, as we see in the following quotes. Midge, a community relations specialist in Ohio, said of her childhood, "*I was not overly protected and definitely not considered 'special.' I was an equal member of the family with chores assigned as my responsibility. I can't even remember not being included even when I had to be carried.*" Sally Smith, a Wisconsin housewife, felt the same way, "*I really was not that 'babied' which I think was good. I was treated quite normally by family. I did many household chores as my mother worked, and I was home alone for several years at beginning of disability (age seventeen).*" Yana DaShana, who uses a wheelchair because of polio, said of her parents, "*They were very encouraging. They allowed me to test my limitations and to venture into areas 'handicapped' usually don't go. After my hospital stay, I was back to washing dishes and doing my share of the ironing.*" Summer related, "*My parents were outstanding adapting to my disability. I never felt that I was less or more than my brothers....I had jobs like cleaning drawers, making school lunches for the next day, writing checks for bills, and scraping the plates to put in the dishwasher—like all children. I didn't want to do it.*" This last remark implies a sense of camaraderie among siblings which cannot help but enhance acceptance as the children either work together at the assigned tasks or conspire on methods of evasion.

Whether the Differently Abled child is truly accepted as she is and treated as an equal member of the family seems to be closely related to the amount of responsibility for household chores she is expected to assume. A lack of real dependence upon the contributions of Easy Goer and Aphrodite can be inferred from their comments. A thirty-nine-year-old supervising clerk from New York, Aphrodite said, "*I could do whatever I wanted to to help in the house.*" Easy Goer, a twenty-eight-year old rehabilitation counselor who has cerebral palsy, said that although she always had chores and responsibilities, "*I always seemed to offer because they were not strictly enforced.*"

It is easy to see the ambivalence of these parents' expectations and, by implication, regard for the feelings of their Differently Abled child, in contrast with the visible optimism of both the parents' expectations and their offsprings' self-esteem in the following quotes. Nancy, a twenty-year-old student from Missouri, said, "*I was ex-*

pected to contribute certain chores to the family just like anyone else. My parents had a very healthy attitude, and I thank them for it! Since I am an only child, I had plenty of opportunities for chores—washing and putting away dishes, vacuuming, setting the table, cleaning my room, folding clean clothes." Poodle Gal, now a mother herself, "*Was made to learn how to dust, do dishes with one hand—sitting sideways beside the sink in my wheelchair, how to scrub floors with a regular mop and a bucket of water. I did the ironing for my family and other people. By the time school ended, I could cook and run a complete house, thanks to my family for making me do things for myself and learn how to be more self-reliant.*" Jenny Jones, a twenty-eight-year-old claims representative from New Jersey, said, "*Duties were found that I could do, such as drying dishes, setting the table, cleaning counters that I could reach. After I learned to drive, I drove my mother shopping and to other engagements. Am asked to drive my sisters to some of their activities.*" Besides the housekeeping duties already mentioned, Shirley O'Hara, a fifty-year-old department store owner and mother of three, said she "*worked in the family business from age thirteen.*"

The important factor here is the parental belief in the Differently Abled child's ability to contribute to the upkeep of the family—to give as well as receive. Implicit in this belief are a valuing of the child for her potential, as well as for her real abilities and a willingness to make the necessary accommodations so that the child can fully share in the family's activities. For example, Jennifer, whose myasthenia gravis set in when she was fifteen, said she received "*at first very special attention with all the problems I had, hospitals, surgery, shots. Felt sorry. Later treated me as others. I had to keep my room neat and help with the dishes. Mostly they went only places I could go to, together—special parks and beaches for handicapped, level church, etc.*"

There seems to be a definite correlation between the equal sharing of family outings and responsibilities and the formation of a positive self-image. From Ursula, who, at the time of her response, was completing a doctorate in educational psychology, nothing was expected in terms of household duties or life goals, and she was seldom included in the family activities; she said, "*As a teenager, I became more insecure and unsure of myself. After I moved out (of parents' home) and had some psychotherapy, my self-image greatly improved. I feel much of the problem is due to the reactions of family and others who make us feel inadequate, ugly and retarded.*" Earlier in this chapter, Mary James stated that she was not permitted to participate in her family's household maintenance because her parents felt they could do things more efficiently, nor was she included very often in family outings; she felt that she had grown up with a low self esteem. Also, we have Daisy D. who was hidden away by her parents and chastised by them for attempting any household chores.

Most of my respondents' parents have had difficult times charting their way through the confusing maze of medical jargon, strange routines and appliances and insensitive stares, without counseling or even concern for their feelings, as they struggled to decide what was best for their child. Those who did well are to be admired. Those who have not done as well should not be condemned, I feel. In my reading and talking to parents of Differently Abled children for this chapter, I have gained a greater appreciation for their difficulties and have lost much of my anger at my mother's mistakes. Hopefully, in the future, supportive services will make the way less difficult for future parents and their Differently Abled children.

Parents clearly do have tremendous impact on the type of self-image a child is forming. Their total acceptance of their Differently Abled child can never totally insulate her/him from the largely negative attitudes she/he will encounter in the outside world, of course, but their contributions to a healthy self-image can provide her/him with the best possible shield to carry through life.

5   Mirrors, Mirrors in Our Minds (Self-Image)

For everyone, a good self-image is important to feeling happy with one's self, reaching out to others, and achieving a sense of competency and success in the world; because most of us receive so much negative feedback about ourselves from society, a good self-image is even more essential for Differently Abled women. Mae Evans, a fifty-year-old California housewife, felt that, *"Being without a sense of Self, without confidence in that Self, is more crippling than being crippled. Without faith in oneself, the really difficult problems cannot be solved."*

Although most of this book has been involved directly or indirectly with the formation of our self-image, the concept of self will be studied more specifically here. Our sexuality is a very important facet of our self-image, both how we feel about ourselves as sexual beings and how we think we are viewed by others. Most women (69) saw themselves as sexual beings. I am happy to report that no one saw herself as completely unsexual; however, five felt that they were neutral.

The comments that follow from a few of these women underscore the relationship between a strong sense of oneself as a sexual being and a positive self-image. Linda volunteered a little self-consciously, *"I am never sure how I appear to myself is the same as how I appear to others."* Charlene, an unemployed hemiplegic in her mid-forties, described herself as "*a real dud,*" then added wryly, "*but my parents' money got me where I am.*" Mary James summed up, "*It all boils down to this: in order to have a positive sexual self-image, one must get reinforcement. One cannot get reinforcement without having the experiences. And one cannot have the experiences without having the positive sexual self-image to pull it off.*"

Fortunately, a self-image is not a static thing. Unlike a book, a piece of music or other artistic endeavor which, at some point, can be considered complete, we have the capacity to continue to grow and change from the moment we are born until we die.

Although body image is, at times, an important aspect of self-image, it is, by no means, the only one. Dahtee, a Massachusetts speech teacher with an unstable form of arthritis, explained how she went about changing her body image. "*I've always had a problem with body image in that I was very heavy as a child....I still have that fat image,...I've decided finally that to change this body image is not to lose weight. The thing to change is the image itself, to change the image to looking at myself as the total woman. I mean, I'm just zeroing in on one little thing when I look at body image and get upset with it...what I am looking at is who Dahtee is and liking who this woman is, and her abilities as well as her disabilities, and getting a more composite picture....When I look in the mirror now, I can see a woman who's gone through twenty-six years of life, and it looks pretty damn good on her.*"

Dolly, a vivacious brunette with cerebral palsy, told how she began changing her self-worth, "*At a certain point, my life changed; at that point, everything was going about as hard as it could get, and I just sat down with myself and said, 'Well, you shut up all your life, and you never really talked when you thought you wanted to,' and I said, 'You got nothing to lose; you just about lost everything.' So I just started to be more outgoing and said what I wanted...and since then, you can't believe the fantastic new job, and I met a lot of friends....I was invited to a wedding. I like to dance, but always I would never dance. I would sit without a partner—all that you go through, that emotional thing—you're at a wedding and you don't have a partner and everybody else does. But the music was playing, and I knew several men there, and I just said 'let's dance.' Well, I had a ball! I was dancing all night....You know, if I didn't take that step, I couldn't have taken other steps.*"

These quotes excite me because they prove that a negative self-image can be changed to a positive one. Changing the way we've been seeing ourselves for most of our life is not easy; it takes consistent effort and self-discipline. But it can be done! Rebecca Burns gave us this example of one Differently Abled women's positive self-image from the pages of *Achievement: "It was a woman, who like me, has a spinal curvature so the two sides of her body don't match. She had decided to wear a bikini, and her statement to the world was: 'I am Racquel Welch as seen through the eyes of Picasso.'"*

A child growing up may develop a poor self-image for many reasons, of course, but becoming Differently Abled either at birth or before the age of fifteen considerably increases your likelihood of doing so. When asked whether, as children, they would rate themselves as prettier, less pretty, or about the same as their peers, twenty-eight women rated themselves as less pretty. Of these, seventeen had acquired their specific physical condition prior to the age of fifteen. Mary James, whose muscular dystrophy began when she was one year old, said that as it progressed she *"was made to wear an ugly brace, use wheelchair more, wear uglier clothes (due to braces)—naturally 'prettiness level' decreased, though was always liked immensely by friends as a 'buddy.'"* E. B. Browning, whose polio occurred when she was nine years old, *"wore two sizes larger than I was because it was easier to dress me."*

Of the seventeen who had become Differently Abled early, four felt better about their appearance by the time they became teenagers. Lola, a thirty-one-year-old Minnesota woman, said, *"After polio* [fourteen years old], *less pretty figure...prettier face-wise after having polio—made effort on hairstyles and make-up to 'compensate' for being handicapped and to compete."*

The feelings of self-consciousness and inadequacy suffered by most teenagers seem to have been intensified by their specific physical condition, however. A total of twenty-nine women had poor self-images as teenagers. When Summer attended a special education grade school, she *"felt totally equal. I did what my friends did and was included in everything. As I reached puberty, new things became important, and I saw myself as undesirable because my disability made me different. I felt inferior and ugly and not as good as the others."*

My own experience was similar. *"One of the gang"* of girls on my block until just before Halloween the year I was twelve, my best friend's mother then informed mine that I would no longer be invited to the annual costume party because *"Dianne would be in-*

viting boys now, and Yvonne just wouldn't fit in." Marlene C., whose polio occurred at the age of seven, felt the same way as a teenager when *"I was more aware of not fitting into social relationships which had sexual overtones. I began to see myself as less pretty and less liked by the opposite sex, except for my close friends. I began to see myself as more intelligent than most, and of being more educated than most, which for a while seemed to be a barrier with people."* Helen W., whose polio occurred at the age ot two, felt *"very awkward as a teen, very different, ungraceful, trying hard to fit in and be like the others. I hated my equipment, was self-conscious, especially with boys. Now this has greatly decreased, but I think I would feel more attractive if I didn't have such a visible disability."*

Of these seventeen Differently Abled before the age of fifteen, twelve had improved their perceptions of their prettiness in relation to peers by the time they were adults.

Some were able to change their appearances. Mary James said, *"College taught me I was intelligent; clothing adaptations, and hair and make-up made me look better; only have difficulty socializing with strangers (I'm too aware of disability then)."* Jane Smith, who has had rheumatoid arthritis since birth, also felt prettier: *"When little or as a teenager, activities were limited, but with physical therapy treatments and fourteen operations, my appearance is greatly improved, thus improving my attitude on life. Losing weight and having prettier clothes and better hairstyles also improved my attitude."*

Others bettered their perceptions of themselves by no longer accepting society's evaluation of them and, instead, concentrating on their individual assets. Summer said, *"I now have learned to accept my disability and to present myself to others as a warm, loving human being."* Shirley O'Hara agreed, *"Attaining some maturity and after marriage and motherhood, I regained a certain amount of self-esteem, and it no longer mattered so much if some rejected me."* Samantha, a California student, stated, *"I have just lately become aware that I am completely acceptable."*

Unfortunately, some women who became Differently Abled after puberty have been diminished by society's perceptions of them. Colleen Moore said, *"Acquiring a disability after I was grown, (twenty-two years) emphasized whatever feelings of inadequacy I had ever had."* Pooh Grayson, whose polio occurred at the age of seventeen agreed, *"My disability is the reason for feeling less pretty from the neck down. I feel about the same from the neck up."*

Mae Evans, a mother of two sons, shared, *"I have a deep fear that I am not attractive to my husband any more, that my changed body and my lack of response during intercourse turns him off. I am convinced of this partly because I look so much older—pain and stress of the last four years have aged my face terribly, I look sixty and I'm only forty-nine* [at the time of the response]*—and partly because of my husband's changed sexual response to me when we are in bed. When it is time for intromission, he often goes flat, and he never had this problem prior to my paraplegia. I'm pretty sure this is a psychological problem—he knows I'm not going to feel anything so subconsciously he thinks he shouldn't feel anything either, which is actually complimentary to me, shows he loves me, but I can't help feeling, 'I wonder how he feels, and is he blaming it on me? He can't give me an orgasm so surely he must think I'm less of a woman,' etc....I will not be able to accept myself as a disabled woman until we work this out....Sexual closeness has always been a terribly important part of my marriage—the spiritual closeness that resulted from the union. We can still recapture that closeness even without my orgasm, but I have to get my self-esteem intact first."*

Others felt that being Differently Abled enhanced their good feelings about themselves. Helen Beach, who became a paraplegic at age twenty-two, said, *"People positively reinforced my ego that I am pretty. When someone compliments me now, I just say 'thank you' without feeling that they are just saying that to be nice. Now, I feel people are being sincere. For a year after my injury I felt terribly inadequate until I learned to do what I can with what I have and to value this."* Jane K., an Indiana tacher who became a paraplegic in her early thirties, said, *"My disability has given me more confidence."* Martha Merriweather, a Delaware widow, credited polio at the age of twenty-two for helping her to *"become more extroverted in order to get people to see past the wheelchair to the individual."* Owen, a Michigan student who became a paraplegic at the age of eighteen and looks like Farrah Fawcett, disclosed, *"I only became really happy with myself after my disability. I'm better in every department! I've seen life turned totally upside down. My values have changed. I live every day as fully as possible."*

As one might guess, one's perception of herself as pretty, strongly related to how well she perceived being liked by others. Although the majority of women (34) felt that, as children, they were liked about the same as their peers, twenty-six perceived that they were liked less. Of these, seventeen also felt that, as children, they were less pretty than their peers. It is encouraging to note, however, that by the time they became teenagers only eight of the seventeen still felt negatively about themselves, and as adults, only three felt this way. Sally Smith explained, "*As a teenager, I saw myself as a person no one would like—a person not really good for or at anything. My disability began at this time, and I became very withdrawn and introverted....After I had brain surgery to correct hydro,....I began to act and feel more like a normal person....I feel more confident since my being in a wheelchair than I did before.*" Penny S., a twenty-six year-old researcher from Canada, said "*My* [negative] *perceptions of myself altered around eighteen when I started college and started to date men. Some very loving and honest boyfriends helped me realize I was a worthwhile and interesting human being...I only wish when I was a teenager I could have spoken to a disabled woman and got some reassurance and info.*"

Some gained a better perception of themselves by developing their mental abilities. Jessica, an interviewer from Texas who became a paraplegic at the age of twenty-five, said she has "*much more security now—know I am pretty and more intelligent than most and that I am liked. Disability has helped bring about inner security and a belief in myself.*" J.J., from New York, felt that her specific condition [cerebral palsy] "*taught me to value my intellect, made me resourceful, a fighter.*"

Generally, the women were inclined to think more highly of themselves than their peers in the cerebral area. As children, twenty-seven women felt they were more intelligent, thirty-six thought they were about the same and only eleven felt less intelligent. At the same period, thirty-one women felt that they had a better sense of humor than their peers, twenty-seven felt about equal, and a mere thirteen felt less humorous. Larkin said, "*I try to encourage and develop creativity and humor rather than tone it down....*" Cindy, a forty-year-old social worker from Wisconsin, felt that although "*initially my perceptions of self were altered drastically as a result of my disability* [polio at age thirteen] *now my sense of humor is more developed, I'm more sophisticated and prettier than as a child or teenager. Creativity has increased 'one hundred fold'.*"

The perceptions of other women on their creativity in relation to their peers were a bit more evenly divided; thirty women felt themselves to be more creative; twenty-seven saw themselves as about the same; and seventeen felt less creative.

Before leaving the influences of childhood on our self-image, I thought it useful to see how much freedom the women had had to develop their sense of style in clothes and appearance while growing up, for, like it or not, appearance and how we feel about it is a significant part of our self-image. When asked how much voice she had as a child in choosing clothes, hairstyles, etc., fourteen women each indicated none whatsoever and very little; nine had some say; and twenty-four had a strong voice in selections. By the time they became teenagers, the women who had no say at all (thankfully) had dwindled to two, and only ten women had very little voice in deciding what they would wear.

These women not permitted to experiment and increase their autonomy while growing up should especially concern us as the following quote from Jay Kirfirst illustrated; *"Many times I was made to feel like a little girl although I was already a teenager—such as the time in high school some girls from a club came to see me on a Sunday. They were dressed 'to kill' in the style of that period, hose, high heels (which I cannot wear even today), and taffeta dresses, jewelry, and make-up. Poor little me in my orthopedic shoes, no hose, only anklets, cotton dress, and then to top it all off, my Mother says for all to hear: 'Oh I forgot to let you put make-up on today!' I nearly died and can still feel it....I also went to a schoolmate's birthday party one Saturday evening. I thought a party meant dressing up so I wore my Easter dress when it wasn't even Easter only to find everyone else in jeans, etc., and casual to say the least."*

I had a similar experience. From the vantage point of adulthood, I can see that my mother being a dressmaker compounded my problem, for I was **always** clothed *"to the nines"* in dresses, white socks, black patent leather shoes, hair ribbons, etc., when my friends were knocking around in jeans and T-shirts.

This additional burden of being dressed differently than peers, when our specific physical condition, to some extent, has already set us apart, cannot help but contribute negatively to self-image during the teens, when conformity to group norms is seen as so important.

When asked about criteria for choosing clothes and hair styles, respondents were about like other women. Thirty-seven women said convenience was important as children. As might be expected, this number dwindled to twenty-two as teenagers and rose again to thirty-eight as adults. Seventeen women said that, as children, the influence of siblings and peers was most important. Again, predictably, the figure doubled during the teen years, then declined to nineteen adults. The teen years, as we know, are a time of great insecurity about one's appearance—a time when the tiniest pimple looms like a mountain—so this quote from Easy Goer, **"As a teenager, I was more aware of my disability and had to compensate by looking and dressing 'like everyone else,'"** expressed feelings common to adolescents, able-bodied or Differently Abled. Also indicative of the extreme need at this time to conform is the reliance upon magazines and clothing catalogs cited by sixteen women as children, with the figure almost doubling as teenagers (31), then increasing only slightly as adults (35).

Only twenty women, as children and teenagers, chose clothes or hairstyles to conceal the disability, and twenty-eight did so as adults. Although the actual number rose with adulthood, when we consider that the number of women who have become Differently Abled in their late teens or early twenties has also increased, proportionally, the figure appears to have actually declined. This may be due to a greater acceptance of self, the bad as well as the good, as we mature, which is lessening the need to camoflage one's specific physical condition.

Another way to enhance a self-concept is through an individual's identification of herself as a member of a particular group. This, to some extent, provides a bulwark of solidarity against the psychological onslaughts of the rest of society against individuals regarded as different. E. B. Browning, who has a master's degree in English, addressed this: **"Society, not my disability, has played a large role in my perception of myself. Until I became my own person, I saw myself as society saw me—and I did not like myself. Society's perception of me is wrong."**

Precisely this type of experience in the sixties prompted Afro-Americans to adopt such slogans as **"Black is beautiful"** in an attempt to regain some of the pride of which they had been robbed by the white majority. Lola saw, **"a lot of parallels between the 'black experience' and the 'handicapped experience'....I think black guys often sense these parallels, if not consciously (and it sometimes is) then unconsciously....Also, before handicapped people became as united and organized into a group, a movement, as they now are, I found a need for identification. I found little in white, able-bodied, middle-class culture I could identify** *with; I found much in the black movement and culture that I could."*

The kind of group cohesiveness that can foster a better self-image in its members is now occurring among Differently Abled people. Anet recounted her growth both as a woman and a Differently Abled individual: *"...being a militant crip has been exciting and rewarding and frustrating. It was about the last part of the sixties, early part of the seventies, when I became very interested in the women's movement and began regarding myself as a feminist. Around that time too, I began thinking of organizations of women with disabilities. After moving to Eugene, I began writing articles for the women's press about women with disabilities in this area....I did get in contact with the disabled women's coalition in Berkeley as a result of my articles, letter writing, activities like that, all alone without anybody really to talk to, to bounce my ideas off, or get feedback from.*

"I also got in touch with the task force for women with disabilities in Seattle, Washington," she continued, *"It was about that time that I met Jan _____ who is a disabled woman, and...started meeting other women in the area with disabilities. There are about ten of us now....It was last April that we were asked to do a workshop on women with disabilties for the Women's Symposium, an annual event...at the University. As a result of that workshop, the Iron Duchess Collective was born, and that is a group of women with disabilities,...we put out a couple of newsletters, set up a couple of sexuality workshops. Our interest was not necessarily in sexuality, but it seemed like the community was expressing an interest in that,...I really feel that my identity exists in being a militant crip. I have been disabled all my life, and I feel that I have an obligation because of my strength and my abilities to do what I can to change the situation of people with disabilities in this society, to elevate their status and improve their attitudes toward themselves and society's attitudes toward them. I know that there are only small things that I'll be able to do, but that's what I want to do."*

Patricia Maher felt a strong sense of identity: *"I am a student at a large university. I am going to have an important role in government. I am adding to the change in attitudes toward the handicapped, and I feel excited, exhilarated and very, very pleased at what I have accomplished and what I am going to accomplish."*

Penny S., who uses a wheelchair because of transverse myelitis, also felt good about her identity as a member of a minority. *"My particular role in society is to change it. At one point in my life when I was in college, I never had any major problems as part of my life. And when I moved out on my own, and I had to find a job, and I had to get there everyday—I guess I found out that there's a lot of shit going on around and around with certain people and that a lot of things have not been done. And then I started to get involved with a national league of handicapped people...about five years ago....And I love it....I guess I'm just one of those people who has to be one of the changers—not one of those who can sit back and say, 'You change it—I agree with you—you go out and do it.' I'm the one that will go out and do it...meet the higher system and talk to him or her....It's a role I'm not going to continue forever. I think I will probably—I hope I will—change because to change is to live."*

Although not all of the respondents saw themselves as such political activists, one can still see some enhancement of self-esteem resulting from the roles adopted by the following women. Carol Sea, another Canadian, saw herself "*as more aware and more of a social/political activist than lots of others; personally, I don't think all disabled people see their roles this way, but I seem to particularly feel that my role is largely one of educator. I have tended to influence the lives of individuals I have met, helping them change their opinions about disabled people. I don't even have to consciously do that. I reveal myself to them as we get to know each other. That's how they learn...if people on the street come up and ask me a very dumb question, which you may know that they are very prone to do, rather than snapping off, to slip my educator role on, and try to straighten them out a little bit about what disabled people are all about.*"

Woodie was more interested in the education of children: "*I like the idea of a child coming up to me when they don't know me and asking me quite honestly about my disability. What really upsets me is when a parent comes along...and retrieves their child whenever they're asking a very honest question....I don't mind about a child asking about my disability....I think that a grownup should have a little more tact.*"

The following are examples of healthy self-concepts. Elizabeth Mark, a former Ms. Wheelchair America, remarked, "*I am not a 'libber' as such, then again, I have always worked under the premise that I am just as good or better than any male or female. Each disabled woman must maintain this attitude if she wants to be a contributing member of society....I enjoy being an involved person. I do not hold my disability against myself. Presently, I am a college instructor and advisor. I am a mother of two fantastic children and have a home and husband to care for. I feel I will never let my shortcomings hinder me from achieving whatever I want to do."*

Joan C., a fifty-three-year-old California teacher, said, *"First and foremost, I am a person—a person who is alive today at this time and in this place, that I have been prepared for it....I am excited about being part of the society in which we live with all of its evils and ills...I'm excited and challenged by the thought that...I can be a part of the solution to the problems of this society...my relationship with my family is very definitely a part of this....I am a wife and a mother....I want to fulfill that role to the best of my ability, to the greatest satisfaction of those I have been placed with....I realize that I fall short many many times, and that's why I'm in a therapy situation in which I can look into myself that I might fill this role more fully, to the greatest capacity that is possible. I'm really working on that. I feel good about that too."* Even though neither Elizabeth nor Joan place a lot of emphasis on minority group identification, it is obvious that much of their satisfaction in life is derived from their self-concepts as women and advocates for changing attitudes about Differently Abled women.

Some women deny that group identification is helpful in strengthening their self-image. Mae Evans believed, *"I don't owe society anything in the way of physical contributions....My first responsibility is to myself, to develop myself the best way I can with whatever circumstances given to me....My role in society, then, is to improve myself, and in so doing, this can affect others in a positive way according to how they receive me.*

"I did not always feel this way," she continued. *"Before my accident, I believed others were more important....After leg loss, I was unable to do for others and so had to find a different measure of self-esteem. I believe my new view is the correct view as nature/God meant because everybody can operate with this veiw. Doing for others can be an important part of self-growth, but we should do for others because we want to, not because we feel we ought to. All humans are alike inside—there can be no different rules for obtaining self-esteem for handicapped and able-bodied....*

"I don't concern myself with feeling 'woman.' I like to feel like me. One-and-a-half years of psychotherapy has made me aware of who I am and who I can be. Good feelings come when I am liking myself (self-esteem) so that I have the confidence to ask others to help me. I find that when I am direct with others (never

pushy) this gives them (if they are unsure of their feelings regarding disabled people) the confidence to forget the disability and see me for what I really am."

Others felt that their self-concept has been forever crippled by their specific disabling condition. Connie L., who has a B.A. in English, recalled, *"I thought of myself as grotesque; I knew that I got good grades but always wondered if that were just some sort of accident, and I'd soon be found out or perhaps if the teachers didn't feel sorry for me, and my grades were an embarrassment at that time anyway....I'm still a teenager in many ways, I'm afraid. I've made some very dear friends, however, who, I know, genuinely like me though I have trouble figuring out why. Of course, most everyone thinks I'm nice, and I do have a good sense of humor. (Aren't all cripples saints?)....Despite my more 'enlightened' opinions, I often feel like a member of an alien species, then compound my self-contempt by feeling guilty about having such views instead of going out hitching cross country or something adventurous like that."* Mary James, thirty years old and single, mourned, *"In the past few years I've grown in my knowledge of myself, my abilities, my socialization, my problems, my appearance, etc., though now I feel it is simply too late. I have been permanently damaged. No amount of my attempting to alter things can change it because what is 'normal' for my age and my partner is too advanced for me. I never went through sexual kindergarten, and now it is college."*

Certainly, how we believe others see us, whether or not our perceptions match reality, greatly affects the way we view ourselves; this is especially true of ourselves as sexual beings. When asked how they thought men and women viewed them, seventeen respondents felt that both saw them as sexual beings. Helen Beach said, *"Because I was married for two years after my injury and because I have a steady boyfriend, I'm sure men and women see me as sexual."*

Fifteen thought both saw them as asexual beings. Connie L., who thought she was seen by both men and women as neutral or unsexual, added, *"I do think it important to stress that the disabled nature of my body has almost totally consumed my image of myself, especially as a sexual being. That I still have my senses intact and ready for pleasure and the sharing of pleasure have not seemed to register with me at a gut level."*

Six other women were uncertain as to how they were perceived. Brillig, an editor at the time of her response, thought that she was considered *"no competition"* by other women and that she was probably seen as either asexual or homosexual by both sexes. A secretary at a rehabilitation facility in Georgia, Annette, explained it this way: "*I am apparently considered very attractive and personable and become acquainted easily with all kinds of people, but a wheelchair apparently prevents my acceptance as a woman and attractiveness does not help in this regard. Probably my age* [fifty-six] *is a factor...*" Deena felt that women generally admired her but that men saw her as a "*cute little girl.*"

Feeling good about your self-image as a sexual being is closely related to a strong sense of one's self as a woman (or a man, as the case may be). When asked what kinds of activities made my respondents feel more like women, there was quite a variety of answers.

Twenty-six named activities traditionally considered as "*womanly*"—dressing up, wearing make-up, shopping for clothes, etc. Helen Beach, listed "*Wearing feminine clothes, taking time with hair and make-up, perfume, delicate jewelry, and being catered to by men....I use these things as tools to keep my ego up and thus avoid severe depression.*"

Fifty-three-year-old Daisy D. agreed, "*Perfect grooming, becoming clothing, CLEAN! Clothing in good repair, good hairstyles, careful make-up, outgoing smiles, good dental hygiene, sincere interest in others.*" Jennifer, whose myasthenia gravis began when she was fifteen, named, "*Shopping, teaching children things, dressing fancy, creative things, sew, knit, crafts, cooking, flowers—growing, arranging,*" then added, "*Frustrates me that I can't do so many creative things myself. Wish someone would help me to be able to do them instead of doing them for me.*"

Twenty women each cited attention from men and sexual activity as the arenas in which they felt most like women. Liz Williams, a single, thirty-one-year-old data transcriber, said, "*When I'm having a conversation, it can be serious, light, or definitely a joke, with a man and I subtly get the message that he's considering me as a woman.*" Helen W., a California occupational therapist, related, "*I feel very much like a woman and good about myself when I am with a man I like very much and who enjoys being with me. I also am aware that I feel more attractive when I'm with an attractive man....How I feel men perceive me, I think, depends, in part, on how I see them. Therefore, if I see men as sexy and attractive, and they enjoy being with me, then I feel more attrac-*

tive about myself." Connie L. generalized, *"Almost any interaction with men that's more than just a hello...And, of course, flirting or joking with men and being given even just a friendly kiss. Anything really where I am treated by men the way they would treat other women."* Summer added, *"...getting hugged and held affectionately; having my men friends come over and cook dinner and just spend time together; also being appreciated and complimented on who and what I am as a person....I have many close male friends, but I feel that as soon as our relationship reaches the point that more should happen it never does, which makes me feel unwomanly."* Melanie Marie, a Florida homemaker, said, *"When a man flirts with me, when I am recognized (with an award) or thanked for a task."* April, who uses a wheelchair because of polio, felt more womanly when *"being clean, having my hair stroked, flirting with a handsome man, being told I have 'a good pussy', sharing ideas and feelings with my favorite man."*

"Fucking," chimed Laura, a twenty-six-year-old Indiana law student, describing what made her feel best. Woodie, agreed, *"Making love to my boyfriend—nothing else comes close,"* as did Samantha, a California student and mother of seven-year-old daughter: *"Lovemaking or setting the stage for lovemaking. I think any good feeling attributes to my 'womanness,' but I do not separate roles into woman roles."* Julia, a twenty-six-year-old artist/homemaker from Alabama, placed at the top of her list, *"Intercourse and oral sex with my husband."* followed by *"cooking and general household duties, shopping with friends, being a good hostess in my home, pretty silk gowns, good music, my collection of house plants."*

Nine respondents were most fulfilled as women by children, housework, and careers. Shirley O'Hara whose polio occurred when she was nine, said, *"Motherhood...also being admired by men and being a success in business made me feel like my own woman, And too, when people would ask my advice and opinions on important matters."* Agreed Pooh, *"I feel more like a woman when...I handle issues with our son...I handle work."*

Three women mentioned that interaction with other women contributed to their good feelings about themselves. Michelle specified, *"Consciousness of women's history and social situations...close friendships with women I care about,"* Sally Smith stated, *"I like to be with other females around my age and participate in some activities they are, i.e. knitting."*

A few other answers are interesting to consider. *"Going to the gynecologist,*" listed Carol Sea. Deena elaborated, "*My large breasts and the recent discovery (by shown by Doctor) that I am a woman and can have intercourse.*" J.J., a teaching assistant, related, "*I put great stock (too much?) in my intellectual ability...as a professional, being female is very secondary.*" Yana Da Shana did not "*think of my activities in this way.*"

All women have been harmed in the past, by society's emphasis on sexual connection with a man, preferably in marriage, as the only real measure of a woman's self-worth: this has been particularly detrimental to Differently Abled women whom society has traditionally assigned to a "no-win" position. First, by treating us as asexual, society has more or less successfully barred us from participation in the only sphere in which it has been deemed we might experience self-worth. Secondly, the societal stress upon physical perfection further reduces our opportunities for feeling good about ourselves in this area. Illustrating this Catch-22 situation is Colette, a twenty-eight-year-old Washington housewife: "*Until I met D. at twenty-three, I felt myself to be homely. I felt that my disability made me ugly and grossly deformed. I'm treated as a nonentity by nearly everyone. If not for my dear D., I would be a total loss.*"

Although the importance of love in our lives cannot be denied, there are other important ways of experiencing fulfillment and increasing our self-esteem as we have already seen and will continue to see throughout this book. Easy Goer was on the right track, I think, when she said, "*Before I want to get involved with another man, I want to know who I am and what I can do so I don't want to get tied up yet before I know this....I think disabled women really need to know more about what they can do and can't do and what they should do before they get involved sexually or any way with a man. So, I think it's important that they do some kind of soul-searching.*"

Mae Evans, mother of two sons, described for us her individual steps in soul searching: "*My first concern as a disabled woman is to accept the disability so I can eliminate the tensions involved in fighting it, so I can get on with my life,...First, I had to accept myself as a human being, something I had never really done before the accident. Then, I had to accept myself as a woman, find out what it means to have been born female and what it means to be a woman today. And next, what it means to be disabled. I am working on that now, going through all the grief...and experiencing all the other feelings necessary to a complete understanding of the situation.*" Reflected Liz Williams,

63

who uses a wheelchair because of cerebral palsy, "*I think I've always felt I was going to have to put ninety percent extra effort into things than other people. No matter how big or how small a thing, that if I didn't do something, nothing would happen. I had (have) to take the initiative. I don't think I realized as a child just how much of a push I was going to have to make and often without anyone helping me in my efforts. What I'm trying to say is just because I may have put 100% effort into something it didn't ensure success.*"

The following are examples of two quite different positive self-concepts. "*Continuing on the subject of self-images,*" Rebecca Burns said, "*my boyfriend sent me pajamas for Christmas which had a rather low square neck, and I asked my cousin to take my picture in them, posing in bed with some cleavage showing...I had her take a picture of my stomach,...exposed all the way down to where the pubic hair begins, also exposing the lower part of my breasts...almost up to the nipple. Another picture I asked her to take was of me lying on my side with my bottom showing, wearing red pajamas. That picture turned out extremely well. I don't really look that good. I send these pictures to him...one a month and titling them Miss November, Miss December and so forth. All rather tongue in cheek, but it's been fun....He's very responsive and appreciative, complimentary....*"

E. B. Browning gave us something valuable to consider in her statement, "*I feel like a woman all the time, and when I act that way I have a better time. Being a woman is fun; being a disabled woman is exciting because no one knows what to expect from you.*"

One can only conclude, after reading all the statistics and quotes in this chapter, that Differently Abled women are faced with all the same obstacles and pressures as are able-bodied women in the development and maintenance of a positive self-image in today's society. Our specific physical condition is an added factor, to be sure, both by its very nature in limiting our physical mobility and to a far greater extent by the responses of others—family, peers, and society in general—to it and, therefore, to us. It is, nevertheless, merely one element to be considered as part of the whole picture comprising a self-image. Some of us regard it as an unfavorable facet; others do not. Despite major disabling conditions, some have very positive concepts of self; other's self-images are hopelessly marred by almost trifling physical imperfections.

E. B. Browning summed it up beautifully for us, "*Disabled women have it no harder or easier than other women; some of us are happy—some, not; some of us are successful—some, not. The thing I abhor the most is not my disability but society's view or perception of me because of my disability—that is what handicaps me. True, I am severely disabled, I have a low economic status, I cannot live an unassisted life, but I live as busy, successful, useful, fulfilling a life as most people do—and more so than many. And it is not 'faith' that keeps me going, it's reality; the reality that being disabled is not a curse—a fate worse than death, it's not a burden—it is simply a different way of life. It has its happy times and its sad, its hard times and easy. If I were not disabled, how many men would want to 'take care of me,' how many men would offer to carry me outside to see the eclipse of the moon? If you are not disabled, would it mean as much to be called a 'foxy lady' or be told you have sexy suggestive ways when I did not even know I had ways?!'*

Getting to Know You (Relationships)

Hot Wheels, a thirty-five-year-old divorcee and mother of a seven-year-old son, felt she had *"to break a barrier before people are really friendly."* Deena agreed, *"I feel I must continue to prove my age and capabilities before people around me will accept me. I feel this is wrong, but in today's society people tend to look upon us as being retarded and having no feelings."*

"My life is so full, there are so many things now, I have so much to do, so many friends, so many people calling me, so many contacts that it feels like more than I can do, and I get too tired. I guess it's an embarrassment of riches in a way. I had so many years of famine when my life was pretty boring that I don't know how to handle the feast," reported Rebecca Burns.

Interactions with others will be explored in this chapter. Although the main focus will be relationships with men, the discussion will not be limited to conventional dating situations.

Some women were concerned about our public image and the way it is shaped by the media. Lola described, *"One thing I've seen very very often that I object to is the use of the word, 'invalid' and the depiction of the handicapped as an invalid. More and more on T.V., I see a scene like this—there's an invalid wife in a wheelchair, whose husband gives her only the most chaste of kisses on her forehead, who sleeps in her own room,...and whose husband is now messing with another woman. The husband's dialogue goes something like this, 'You see, since Alice got sick, had her accident, I've been so lonely and frustrated. It's horrible. I suppose I should be feeling guilty, but I'm only human. I'm still a man,' (implying that she's not still a woman)....The effect on our sexual image has got to be bad, bad, bad! If we are depicted as sexless, how can anyone have a different image of us?...I get the impression that handicapped sexuality seems subject to the same handling as romance scenes between blacks, and especially between blacks and white, used to be—really taboo...except, I suspect, for completely opposite reasons. With blacks, it was because people had a sterotype of them being so super-sexed somehow that a love scene would be too potent on T.V. With the handicapped, the stereotype has always been that there was little or no sexuality to portray."*

Mae Evans was also concerned about *"the way society views the handicapped. Parents hiding their imperfect children; people saying 'Why should I make my place of business available to the handicapped; they never come here'....Editing the handicapped out of our lives because it's easier to not see them than it is to include them....Society stereotypes the disabled just as it stereotypes old people, blacks, youth, motorcycle drivers, and women. Any breaking down of any stereotypes in any group is going to help other groups break their stereotypes."*

In the following pages, the effects of this treatment of Differently Abled women on our relationships will be seen.

When asked to consider their casual relationships with men, fifty-one women rated them satisfactory while twenty-four found them unsatisfactory. Five felt their relationships unsatisfactory because they were treated just as friends and not as women. Nancy, a twenty-year-old Missouri student, said, *"General relationships with men are both satisfactory and unsatisfactory because on one hand I have good close male friends who I can talk to, but unsatisfactory in that I have yet to have a solid give-and-take relationship with a man (sexual and emotional)."* Sandy Mitchell, an assistant editor for a braille magazine, complained, *"My friendship relationships (with men) are fine, but it's the love or whatever relationships I'm dissatisfied with. I never seem to find any permanence, which is what I seek,"* then added, *"But if the relationships don't last, they are usually pretty good."*

Five women rated relationships unsatisfactory because the time they were able to spend with men was insufficient. Connie L. did not *"have very many relationships with men. I'm intimidated by them. What relationships I do have are mainly with husbands or lovers of my female friends. I have virtually no relationships, even of the most platonic sort...that I've gotten into on my own. My relationships with my father are loving but not intimate so they were not a help in building relationships with other men.*" Jay Kirfirst revealed, "*Have never, other than by mail, had any* [relationships]. *Ninety-nine percent make me nervous, though it used to be 100%.*"

Another five named male chauvinism as the cause of their relationships being unsatisfactory; three felt they had often been used as sex objects. Patricia Maher thought she was seen as merely "*a welcome mat; love me and leave me.*" Lola found that this type of man often wanted "*the relationship confined to a merely sexual one,*" and categorized him as "*(1) the married man; (2) the 'don't want to be seen with her in public' type; and (3) the 'I'll see her as long as we don't become emotionally involved' type—he sets strict limits to the relationship, makes sure you understand them (if he's honest). He may attempt to just plain offer money in exchange for sex.*"

In an interesting switch from our depiction ,as sexless by the general media, some men's magazines have, in recent years, discussed Differently Abled women as sexual novelties. Although in my younger years I sometimes exploited this curiosity, I soon realized that such superficial attraction actually deters the formation of any meaningful relationship because as soon as these men discover we don't possess any super—or otherwise novel sexual powers, they're gone.

In a more positive way, being Differently Abled can be advantageous. Twenty-eight women thought they were seen favorably by men. Colleen Moore, a thirty-three-year-old special consultant and mother of two, found that her "*wheelchair is a turn-on—if not that, at least an ice-breaker.*" Sandy Mitchell, who uses a wheelchair because of muscular dystrophy, said, "*Many men find me attractive and fun to be with. Some are scared by the chair, and some are scared by the strength of my personality—but then that attracts many men too.*" Shirley O'Hara "*was told in later years that the disability—plus my personality and attractiveness—was a combination that was hard to resist,*" and believed, "*The partial dependency is flattering to a man's ego.*" Jane Smith, a vocational rehabilitation counselor in Pennsylvania, felt men perceived her as "*friendly and good looking with concern for their feelings—someone who listens to their story, whether good or bad.*"

Along with the extroverted personalities we often develop, we may have the additional asset of being in the right place at the right time. Samantha, who incurred a spinal cord injury at the age of twenty-three, observed, "*Most of the men I meet are through work—there is initially curiosity and some sympathy—but we get down to business very quickly, and I am accepted. I think mostly due to my own and others' liberation I am no longer the 'cute little thing.'* "

Thirty-two women felt they were perceived unfavorably by the men they meet. There was the mild discomfort described by Jane K., "*Men are slightly afraid and wordless,*" and the outright patronization Lola has heard from many men, "*Gee, you're beautiful even if you are crippled.*"

On the other hand, some of us may be perceived unfavorably for reasons quite separate from our specific physical condition, as describd by Scarlett, a thirty-eight-year-old homemaker and college student, "*Unsatisfactory moments* occur during discussions. I tend to be socially and politically interested and opinionated—men find this irritating at times.*"

Much of the men's discomfort stemmed from the old "*saintly*" image we have been trying for so long to shed. Jennifer believed that "*most men feel uncomfortable because I convey the image of someone whom they cannot smoke around or tell dirty jokes in my presence.*" Pooh said, "*They initially seem uneasy and afraid of doing something which might hurt or offend me.*" Owen, a student and freelance writer, had "*the general feeling that most of the males encountered view me as being very delicate and fragile though I do not purposely try to convey this image.*"

The other stereotype—that we are asexual—is the cause of numerous unfavorable perceptions on the part of men. Easy Goer said, "*I feel men perceive me as a 'cute' kid and as a good friend or buddy. This makes me feel extremely upset and inadequate.*" Woodie, who has spina bifida, also responded, "*After they get to know me, they like me but only as a friend—nothing more.*" Mary James noticed that men "*seem to avoid physical contact and seem to view me as very desirable as a friend but not as a woman. I also see a fear in men toward my physical attributes and appliances. This is difficult to overcome.*" Mrs. Lewis, a retired teacher from Arizona, put it wryly, "*'Hey, let's do her a favor, taking her out,' or plain rejection.*"

Fifteen women felt that men's perceptions of them were neutral, Melanie Marie thought she was perceived "*initially as a disabled person; after an introduction and conversation, as a woman who happens to use a wheelchair.*" Owen summed up, "*I meet a wide range of males, some are simply curious, some are religiously based, and some are just friendly. There is a certain sort of male who can accept a woman in a wheelchair, and there is the male who can accept the walking woman."*

Many women who became Differently Abled as teenagers or adults noticed real changes in how they were treated by men before and after the accident or illness. Brillig, whose polio occurred when she was twenty, stated, *"I felt like the whole world had declared war on me. Men were less direct than women. They often seemed to want to know if I could still feel physically. They obviously didn't think I felt humanly."* Mae Evans had a different perception of the changes, *"It's easier to talk to me now because the wheelchair both interests and saddens them. It brings out their feelings."*

Then, speaking more from her own viewpoint, she continued, *"As a sexual being, I feel more comfortable with men now than I used to. I think the wheelchair removes the threat of male-female interaction which goes on sub-consciously....I know there is absolutely no way a man is going to imagine me in bed with him, that can be put aside and we can just be friends. Before paraplegia, I did not have men friends just to talk to. Now I have several....It makes me feel good that they think I'm interesting to talk to, that they like me for me."* Julia, also spinal cord injured but at the age of sixteen, agreed that she noticed now *"men seem to want to get to know me better rather than take me straight to bed. Most men seem to appreciate my 'SPUNK.'"* Michelle, who has been dealing with the effects of multiple sclerosis for about the last five years, said, *"I am perceived as S.'s wife. They act jolly, sometimes they're more comfortable because the burden that's on them to 'conquer' all women is less. But that means a wheelchair—sexless too."*

The following quote is interesting because it is the goal of many feminists: yet when **we** are regarded in this manner it is distasteful for it smacks of the old neuter stereotype. Marta Lin, who became a paraplegic at the age of thirty-five, said, *"Most men regard me as a good gal, brave (which I am not) and an easy person to be with....They stop seeing you as a women—still sexual—just a person."*

Only five women detected little or no change in their casual relationships with men. Marie R. reported, *"I became disabled when I was dating a steady boyfriend. He never once hesitated to continue seeing me."*

Most respondents spent more recreational time with able-bodied men (45) than Differently Abled men (9). Thirty felt that they were treated differently by each group. Of these, eight women believed that Differently Abled men regard them as sexual beings whereas able-bodied men do not. Melanie Marie said, *"Disabled men realize immediately that I am a woman—no initial hesitation."* Beth, a Washington homemaker, made this comparison: *"With disabled men, I am 'like' them; with non-disabled men, I am 'different.' It's hard for them to get past the disability."* Liz Williams, who uses a wheelchair because of cerebral palsy, agreed, *"I think able-bodied men think of me as a good likeable person, but I don't think they even consider me as datable. Disabled men consider me datable though. Presently, and not by choice, I spend leisure time with disabled men."* Penny S. related, *"Some disabled men have told me I should sleep with them because I am disabled too."* Eight other women spent their leisure time with Differently Abled men while twelve passed it with both.

Carol Sea and Rebecca Burns held opposite views on the nature of Differently Abled men: Carol observed, *"Disabled men are more inclined to spend time with me but are more shy;"* Rebecca said, *"I feel very good about myself as a counselor....This is my great strength apparently in relating to the opposite sex. Right now I'm cultivating all that I can on a very casual social basis. I call up disabled men under some pretext..., and I kind of guide them into talking about their fears and their problems as much as they want to, and I'm just really amazed at how they open up to me."*

Seven women expressed a preference for able-bodied men. Mary James said, *"Know very few disabled men. Am not attracted to any (perhaps only one) as more than acquaintance due to age and interest differences."*

Some cited practical reasons for their preferences. Lola, who uses a wheelchair, expressed some of my concerns in the following: *"I realize this may sound prejudicial, but if they were disabled to the degree I am...there wouldn't be much we could do together socially or sexually....I need help with many things, and they couldn't provide it. Sexually, I'm not that limited with someone able-bodied. This may sound rather graphic, but someone has to be on top, someone has to move their hips. If neither person could move, it seems to me the sexual part would be limited to little more than mutual masturbation.*

"If I was less seriously disabled...and completely independent," she continued, *"I would be very prone to seek out*

disabled men who were also independent. It would be a natural thing to do—we'd have been through a lot of the same things and, consequently, I'm sure, be more likely to understand each other better and treat each other better." Easy Goer voiced concern "*about mixed kinds of relationships where there's one disabled individual and one non-disabled....Is it going to be a give and take kind of relationship, or is it going to get to be that the non-disabled person has to help the disabled person?...You see, I like to go out a lot, I like to be mobile. Now I need a certain amount of help, and if I could do that with somebody, then that would be good.*"

Fear of perpetuating the stigma was also a consideration. Easy Goer continued, "*I feel that if I marry a disabled person...I'll be kind of categorized as a disabled person and not looked upon as a person.*" Annette, a fifty-six-year-old widow, told of her experience: "*Since I come in contact with men in rehab. work, they seem to regard me as another quad with no sensation and don't realize I am a polio and do not have the problems of spinal cord injury. Able-bodied men see me as a 'thing'; disabled men reject me as I believe it helps their image to be seen with able-bodied women only.*" Summer felt that "*disabled men tend to be less friendly than able-bodied men because of the myth that disabled people should stick with their own kind.*"

A great testimonial for a Differently Abled man came from Martha Merriweather: "*My present sexual partner is a paraplegic Afro-American and has been the most understanding of my needs and the most able to fulfill them even though he is not capable of intercourse. He makes me feel like a woman and sure knows how to make love. I actually prefer going to bed with him over and above the able-bodied men I have known. Our need for extended sexual activity is mutual and gratifying.*"

For eleven other respondents, race was not an important factor in the formation of relationships. In a truly universal spirit, Penny S. said, "*I don't really care what a person's race is. I have slept with a Black man, a Chinese man, many disabled men and many non-disabled men.*" Pooh Grayson agreed, "*Race is not a consideration for me in being attracted to the opposite sex.*" Joan C., a bilateral amputee from California, disclosed, "*Presently, I think I would be open to a relationship with anyone if there was good communication.*" Commented Sandy Mitchell, "*Race and cultural difference too often gets in the way. I have noticed that black men are very sexually attracted to me; I'm not sure why. But they also tend to come on too strong for my particular lik-*

ing. I prefer subtlety."

Twenty-four women had had little contact or experience with men of other races and felt that they had more in common with their own. Yvonne Winters, who, incidentally, is Afro-American but preferred Caucasian men, remarked, *"I would imagine that it's due to the experiences of the individuals being similar, especially educationally."* Kathryn, a divorcee, left it open-ended—*"I like men who have same church views and my culture. I'm comfortable with them. If I found one of another culture that I was comfortable with, it would be O.K. but so far have not found him. Who knows what is ahead?"*

Thirteen preferred men of their own race due to upbringing or religious/moral convictions, and only three expressed a dislike for men of other races.

In today's society, there are many obstacles to be overcome in order for men and women, Differently Abled or not, to be able to relate freely and openly with each other. Mae Evans highlighted only one of these in her indictment of *"men who put women down for whatever reasons. This includes organized church throughout the ages and contemporary people like the Billy Grahams, the Pope, and all others who quote from the Old Testament to prove that women are the servants of men and that sex feelings outside of marriage are unacceptable. I am really angry that women have been made to accept their ideas because God says it's true. 'Do unto others' has been pushed because that's what men want....The 'love thyself' portion of Jesus' message seems to be soft-pedaled. A true understanding of 'love thyself' can free women—and men—from society-imposed stereotypes."*

Larkin noted another aspect of tradition: *"I think women and men have been raised to behave in ways that cause each other pain....About three years ago, I went on a trip to Toronto for a weekend with two women and two men. We all crashed in the same room at the Holiday Inn. I think it was the first time I realized how differently us women would have acted if the men hadn't been along....Men and women have been trained to act very differently, and when we're together it's really hard to be real people."*

I think there's a growing awareness that we are all just people attempting to grow and love in what often seems to be an alien world, and this acceptance can only be good for those of us who are Differently Abled. Meanwhile, the current tradition of changing roles is a difficult period for male-female relationships. Penny S. put it this way, *"I am a feminist, and I find most men can't accept a truly equal woman. I spend a lot of time fighting with men about women's rights."*

Of course, being a Differently Abled woman can add other complications to the already complex process of forming love relationships. One of these is our internalization of society's labels. Penny S. continued, *"I guess my most pressing concern is that the disabled women that I meet don't seem to care that they are considered non-sexual beings and are getting ripped off....I find it really difficult to deal with other disabled women as my equals because they tend to be much more passive; they have observed the situation they're in, and they can't do anything about it."* Lola, whose polio occurred when she was fourteen, in " *a conversation I had with a classmate only a couple of years after I had polio,"* showed us how early the asexual stigma can be internalized. *"She had had polio as a baby. I was lying, complaining about my lack of dates, which were few and far between, and she told me that this was something I would have to accept—that most men won't go out with someone handicapped. As a high school senior, she had never had a date...she was averagely attractive and considerably less handicapped than I....She seemed so accepting, so unconcerned. I guess I ended up feeling that if she could really accept this,...then she was probably better off than me because I couldn't accept....Who would end up leading the happier life—her, with the acceptance or me, the one who keeps trying, keeps getting frustrated. It seems that she never experienced some of the lows that I had, but it also seems like she never experienced some of the highs. I wondered if her acceptance of a lack of male relationships was sort of bred into her because she had almost always been handicapped. I know most of my other handicapped classmates at the time seemed to feel as she did....For a long time, this created a division between me and a lot of handicapped individuals. I felt alone, alienated, that I must really be an oddball because of my physical and psychological sexual drives that were still very intact....Handicapped women are beginning to understand how thoroughly they have been brainwashed by parents or society."*

As this quote and much of my research suggest, society, parents, and our own incorporation of their perceptions of us, make some Differently Abled women view themselves as asexual or immoral when they do feel sexual. This suppression of normal feelings seems to occur more in congenitally Differently Abled women, probably because they have been exposed to more negative influences before their self-images have been sufficiently formed.

Another deterrent to our forming relationships with men is fear, which can take many forms. Mary James admitted: "*My natural impulse when touched is fear (of not being able to respond adequately, etc.); and, therefore, I fail to encourage the situation. I have a terrible fear of rejection, and this is accentuated by the fact that I cause most of the rejection by my own fear! A fierce snowball....The only 'hope' is a superunderstanding and instructing and loving man who will help me through this.*" Then she gave the following illustration: "*When I was twenty-five, I met my male friend....We've had five years of a growing, loving relationship. However, it was purely platonic. Now he is engaged to another. The engagement has forced us into gut-level communication on the only subject we've never tackled: sex. 'Why have you never touched me? Are you afraid of what might happen if you get turned on?....' may have been some of my questions; however, his honest replies are what awakened me: 'I was waiting for you to give the sign. Yes, I was scared, but I was not turned off by your physical differences. And I was willing to try anything. But I was waiting for your sign....'*

"*The unbelieveable thing is this: All the time I thought I was 'giving him the sign'....I drew on all the resources I had to make myself more sexually desirable. Looking back, these were very minimal. When I touched him, I made sure I would not appear too forward or sexual. I withheld sexual comments because I didn't want him to think that was all I thought of. And I was patient. I figured we'd get around to the physical aspects when our relationship developed more. After all, I didn't want to push it too far because I might lose him since a physical relationship with me would no doubt be repulsive to him, and I totally would understand that! I see now how screwed up I was—and am.*"

She continued: "*There is a vital need for self-improvement courses, self-image courses, sex education, and the like in orthopedic schools, literature, recreation programs...for the handicapped. Also, there is a desperate need for housing for the handicapped where sexual activity, dating, and socialization in general can occur without nursing home or parental control or observation when a person reaches adulthood.*" In illustrating the need for these programs, she said, "*I thought 'dating' had full implications of: leave at eight, go to movie, park and neck, etc.—no source of a norm.*"

Daisy D., touching on another very real fear experienced by many Differently Abled women, said "*When very young, I was afraid to admit I needed feeding and other help. As I matured, I became more practical and simply explained it, then left it up to him.*" This is something I, too, have wrestled with over the years and used to limit myself to ordering in restaurants only foods which didn't have to be cut rather than to ask for help. Fortunately, some maturity and a kind, considerate boyfriend in the past few years have enabled me to enjoy a few good steaks.

The fear of possibly being hurt is also a very real fear. Jessica, a thirty-one-year-old divorcee, shared her feelings: "*First of all, I...close myself off to possible relationships. I think it goes more into being hurt in previous relationships which affected me as a sexual being....now, with me the idea is not to get too involved with anyone. That's sort of bad because it could possibly stop something, a relationship with another human being, sexually or in any other way...before it ever really got started.*"

At this time, I am facing this fear of future hurt after having broken up recently with the man I had lived with for over a year and had hoped to marry. The natural tendency is to retreat deep down inside yourself and not to reach out or share with anyone else for fear of another rejection. We must resist these tendencies, however, because not to do so may allow us to escape hurt and rejection, but we may also escape happiness and fulfillment. I was recently given a book that has aided me through this most difficult time. It is called *How to Survive the Loss of a Love: Fifty-eight things to do when there is nothing to be done*, by Melba Colgrove, Ph.D., Harold H. Bloomfield, M.D. and Peter McWilliams, available by order no. 22270 from Simon and Schuster, 630 Fifth Ave., New York, N.Y., 10020.

Not to be considered by men as datable is a problem mentioned before in this book as a very real obstacle for Differently Abled women in the formation of male-female relationships. Martha Merriweather, a forty-three-year-old widow, stated, "*I am a mother, I will be a journalist eventually, and I am also a female looking for male companionship....the third role causes me concern because of attitudes on the part of able-bodied men. I find that I make friends rather easily but that I am not considered dating material because of my wheelchair. In fact, I've had men say to me, 'I wish you weren't in a chair,' to which I respond, 'So do I'.*"

Jenny Jones, a paraplegic since birth, complained about the lack of spontaneity: *"Well, it wouldn't be like 'Why don't you come out for a drink?' type of thing. I haven't had that happen, and I would think that that's a very common type of thing to happen, so in that respect I guess I would be treated differently."*

Larkin made a good point about this whole business of not being regarded as we wish to be when she said, *"You can't feel responsible for the other person. You've got to say what you want as clear as you want, and then it's up to them to flip out or freak out or whatever they want."* Helen Beach agreed, *"I'm not asked out so often—so I'm more assertive and am quite clear if I want a deeper relationship."*

A number of women spoke of the quality and endurance of relationships. Helen W. shared, *"I guess I'm most concerned about a stable long-lasting relationship. I'm much more discriminating in terms of my sexual relationships as I get older. Prior to my first sexual involvement, I did wonder about being able to satisfy my partner; that is no longer an issue, but I'm looking for a more committed relationship, with sex just being a part of that commitment."* Lola was *"also concerned aboud finding partners with whom to have a more complete relationship as opposed to a purely sexual relationship...and I feel with a disabled person this is particularly difficult. I feel that there are many people who are willing to have limited relationships with me but are afraid of getting too involved....I want, preferably in the same relationship, a social relationship, going out places together, doing things together, sharing experiences....Like I'm sure everyone feels, I'd like to find someone to love and to be loved by.*

"Years ago," she recalled, *"my only criteria for choosing was finding a man physically attractive....While I'm getting choosier, or trying to get choosier, time will tell. If you go through a month or a year of desperate loneliness as I have at times in the past, I will probably revert to taking what I can find—partial relationships as opposed to no relationships at all."*

Penny S. was troubled about the rut she seemed to have fallen into in relationships with men, *"I just can't seem to keep a good relationship going. It always screws up....I guess I love it when I'm in love. I've started a new relationship, and I'm at the top of the world and feel that nothing can go wrong, and you go around and look pretty and—I don't know—there's a certain glow about you. I like that feeling. I wish it could continue for me...find someone I could have a long-term relationship with....I don't expect the romantic type of love to last;...I'd just like to have some kind of good love last."*

Anet shared her experience in creating a solid relationship: *"I guess my present concern is building a really good ideal relationship with the man I'm living with. We've been together for eleven years, and we've gone through some really hard times together, and we've drifted away, been very close, and now we're trying to work on having something consistent and something we can count on, both of us, when we really want and need it. It's like being able to live your own life and having him live his own life and still having a really strong life together. It's hard work; it's not something that just comes out of someone's romantic fantasies. There's a lot of talking you have to do, a lot of working out of bad feelings that come from nowhere and some bad feelings that come out of somewhere. Anyway, we're working on it...."*

The women spent their recreational time with men in a large variety of ways, proving that relationships do, in fact, occur despite difficulties. The largest number of women associated with men at parties (46) with sexual activity (40) following closely. Other activities with men included movies (37); spectator sports (29); bars and church and other types of social clubs tied at (27); dates (23); table games such as Scrabble or Monopoly (22); participation sports such as wheelchair basketball or table tennis (14); study dates(13); eating out or hosting dinner parties (12); picnics (9); double dates (7); camping (6); swimming (3); watching T.V. and shopping each done by (2). Other activities with men mentioned were study groups, political activity, consumer groups, billiards, dances, and snowmobiling.

When asked if they required a partner's physical assistance to participate in these activities, twenty-seven women indicated they did not. Helen Beach, a student and writer, stated, *"When I first meet men, I'm concerned with how they first perceive me in my chair—a lot of people I meet are going to think I'm going to be dependent, docile, and I tend to be overly independent. Solutions for me are talking to people and just letting them know that...I like to take care of my own needs—that I need a certain amount of space for myself because that's how I am as a person. But sometimes it's difficult for me to accept help from other people,...and this is because I can do it myself and I don't like to be pushed around. Even though it's my chair, it feels like an extension of me, and it feels, sometimes, to me like I'm being pushed around so I just make it real clear to people...if I'm not feeling comfortable with being pushed that I'd rather get on going under my own steam and that I need the exercise."*

Thirty-seven said they did need some help, all but two of whom required some type of mobility assistance such as pushing a wheelchair, helping transfer into a car, etc. Seven also required more extensive assistance such as feeding, undressing, etc. Five women needed help with positioning for sexual activity. Ursula's partner usually aided by *"putting chair in my van, assistance at times to make me more comfortable, and in sexual activity, some movement of my body. At first, afraid of hurting me. With time, very relaxed—even to the point of helping me in bathroom."*

When asked about their degree of comfort with this, twenty-seven women felt comfortable requiring their partner's aid, twenty-six felt slightly uncomfortable, and only four felt very uncomfortable. In reply to the question about their perceptions of their partners' comfort levels in assisting them, thirty-four respondents thought the men were comfortable with it, twenty thought they were slightly uncomfortable, and only one said her partner was very uncomfortable.

Following are some comments on the comfort issue: Helen Beach said that her partner was *"happy I was more dependent on him. I was miserable about that."* Melanie Marie noticed, *"He got more comfortable as we fell in love."* Summer agreed, *"When I just met him, he had never known anyone who was severely disabled. After seeing me interact with other people and asking me a million questions and interacting with me on a one-to-one basis, he is aware now of my physical limitations. Also, as we become closer emotionally and intellectually, he is more comfortable doing things for me—and it is easier for me to ask him to do things."* Julia commented similarly, *"He was comfortable but curious, and was afraid of hurting me physically. I'm very petite, and he thought I was delicate."*

Typical dating situations may be delayed or cause difficulty or awkwardness for some Differently Abled women. Three, all of whom had been Differently Abled from birth, had never experienced a real date. Jenny Jones said, *"Because, I think, of the acceptance of my family and close friends, I think it* [specific physical condition] *has played only a small part. I think the fact that I have had so little dating experience has kept me from testing these perceptions as they pertain to the perceptions of the opposite sex."*

The overall average age of my respondents' first date was seventeen years, but there was a wide discrepancy between those who were Differently Abled at the time of their first date (19 years) and those who were not (14 years). Liz Williams, who went on her first date at the age of nineteen, recalled. *"During my early teens, reading all the articles on dating, popularity, etc., for a long time I thought that maybe I really was just a late bloomer, and that's why I wasn't part of all the action. As I tried to follow much of the advice in those books and articles, and nothing was bringing results, I slowly realized having a disability had more problems than I thought."*

Our beginning to date later than our able-bodied peers is probably related not only to our often reduced opportunities to socialize but also to the maturity level of the young men who date us. They must acquire a degree of self-confidence before they can resist the peer pressure to be seen only with the most attractive and are able to appreciate the beauty within each of us. Sandy Mitchell said, *"Younger men (when I was a teenager) were really scared of getting involved."* Daisy D. remembered that when *"pals began serious affairs, I was left out except with the least intelligent and least attractive...was called upon by friends to 'counsel' their petty romantic problems....I liked this but felt left out until older guys took me as serious."*

The sources of partners for my respondents' first dates are interesting to note. Friends from school were the most popular source (36) for the total group; however, of the thirty-eight women Differently Abled at the time of their first date, only eleven went out with school friends, less than one-third as compared to almost half for the entire group. Of the thirty-eight, four went out the first time with friends of siblings while only seven out of the total group cited this source.

Marie R., a Michigan housewife who was not Differently Abled at the time she began dating was the only woman whose first date was with a friend from church.

Women already Differently Abled at the time of their first dates tended to list less traditional sources of them. Two dated friends of friends, and two others dated males who lived in the same neighborhood but did not attend the same schools. Four met their first dates while in hospitals or other rehabilitation facilities. Cindy, a Wisconsin social worker, explained, *"Because he was working on a rehab. unit, he accepted my disability,...he became more involved with me."* Deena, whose first date at age twenty-one was with a camp counselor, said *"Since it was a camp for disabled adults, he liked and trusted me to the point that he felt unafraid*

81

of teaching what I already should have known." More unusual sources of first dates were Amy Bradburn's blind date with a friend of her grandmother, and April's with the nephew of her mother's boyfriend.

Thirty women said that their dates seemed comfortable and fairly unconcerned that they were Differently Abled. Six found the men to be overly cautious and anxious to be helpful. Pooh Grayson, whose first date was a friend from school, rated him "*very accepting and concerned about what he could do for me to make our dates more fun—slightly nervous about doing things right. He became more confident in assisting me. Helping me made him feel important.*" Shirley O'Hara, who was Differently Abled when she had her first date at eighteen, "*thought he felt sorry for me and that is why he asked me for a date. (I refused dates for that reason all through high school unless it was someone I knew well such as a friend of the family.) It seemed he really was interested in me (if I gave him a chance) and not in the fact that I was handicapped.*" Marlene C., whose first date occurred at the age of twenty-four with a Differently Abled friend from school, observed, "*Peers' dates, at earlier ages, were more frivolous, and mine was pretty serious and intense from the onset.*"

Larkin and her friends chose a novel way around the dating game. "*The Rejects started when I was about ten. There was me and a couple of close friends, and we had a party on New Year's Eve and called it the Rejects Ball....It became a yearly event. The school would be having these mass parties where you were supposed to go as a couple, and we were just really thriving on our Rejects Club—not that we were rejected—we were rejecting all that.*"

It is clear that Differently Abled women do not have the same social opportunities in high school as do abled-bodied peers. Our first dates occurred on the average of almost four years later than theirs, and fewer of these dates were with friends from school. A partial reason for this can be attributed to the fact that of the sixteen women who indicated "*other*" sources of their first dates, seven had home teaching and four had attended special education facilities for at least part of their education. It is extremely important, therefore, for Differently Abled adolescents, as well as we, older women, to extend our social circles as wide as possible. For teenagers, this may mean joining Girl Scouts, church groups, community activities, arts and crafts classes at the YMCA, or special interest groups, such as recycling projects.

To counteract the social detriment of even short periods of

segregated education, I envision a *"Buddy System"* (for lack of a better term) through which a Differently Abled teenager would be matched with a buddy of either sex from the local high school. The object of this matching would not be patronizing visits like those suffered by Jay Kirfirst but friendly get-togethers for shopping, movies, sports activities, or just plain rap sessions which would be mutually beneficial. This extracurricular activity should **not** be in any way publicized in the school as *"good experience"* for future nurses, physical therapists, etc., but should include lawyers, housewives, accountants, etc., according to the interests of those being matched.

As we have alredy seen throughout this book, a major concern, voiced by Ursula, is *"finding a sexual partner. My last real relationship ended in June, and I have been quite lonely since. I went through a stage of proving to myself that I could get a man to go to bed with me about two years ago so I am not simply interested in sex but in a sexual 'relationship'....I am not sure as to the solution. I have tried meeting men in many settings. However, I realize this is a problem all women have."*
Hoping to find some useful answers to this rather weighty problem, I asked the twenty-two respondents who married after becoming Differently Abled how they had met their mates. Six had met their partners through introductions by friends or relatives. Carol Sea, married common-law in Canada, said, *"We met at a friend's house party."* Shirley O'Hara, who has been married four times, specified how she met each of her husbands: *"First was a school chum; second, met through correspondence during World War II; third, a vacationer from out of town; and fourth, brother of my best friend."*
Three women met their mates through work. Jennifer, who has since separated from her husband, said that they had met when he *"came to sell some things at the house."* Anet, who is married to a writer, answered, *"He was my attendant for about seven years. He didn't provide personal care but did take over household duties and got me out occasionally."* Three became acquainted with their husbands at gatherings of Differently Abled persons, and three others met through blind dates.
Melanie Marie met her husband at a bar. So did Julia who specified, *"on New Year's Eve. He introduced himself and asked me to go for a ride on his bike."*
There were some unique answers. Although not officially *"married,"* Colette was, nevertheless, at the time of her response, living

with her partner in a stable relationship, and I felt that her account was definitely worth noting. She said, "*We met in the nursing home where I was a resident. My 'darling' was visiting a young man who also resided there. He noticed me in the hall one day, and I looked, according to D., so pretty and attractive that he asked the aides about me. A few days before my birthday (twenty-fourth) this redheaded dude comes walking over to where I'm sitting by the nurses' desk looking all sad and lonely. He asked me what was wrong, could he possibly do anything for me. I answered with as much bitterness as I could drum up, 'No, there is nothing you can do for me!' and I rolled to my room. Several days later, I was sitting in the parking lot watching the late afternoon sun set...D. drove into the lot, saw me and asked if I'd like to go for pizza and beer. I hadn't eaten dinner yet that evening,....so I said 'yes,' sped to my room via my electric wheelchair to wash up, change, and put on some make-up and cologne....On the way, we chatted like old friends.*" Sally Smith met her husband "*on cassette tape through Voicespondence Club.*" Jane Smith chose a different approach: "*I met my husband through an ad in **Accent on Living**, 'wanted male companion for woman in wheelchair'.*"

Although the above represent some novel ways to meet men, it is still quite unlikely that Prince Charming is going to magically arrive on the doorstep ready to carry one off on his white horse—one has to look for him. Therefore, it is wise for Differently Abled women to get out into the mainstream of society where we increase our chances of meeting a wide variety of men. Besides the activities suggested earlier for teenagers, I would add for adults musical and little theater groups. (I am currently involved in a women's theater group.) Even if you don't know a G major chord from your little finger and you're sure you can't act, there are lots of other important things to do in the areas of publicity, tickets, costumes, etc.

Involvement in political activity is also a great way to meet new friends. Besides already sharing an enthusiasm for your particular candidate or issue, working together on a common project makes it easier to break the ice and start conversations. There are always lots of telephoning, addressing envelopes, writing speeches, leafletting, etc., that we can do as well as anyone. A side benefit not to be overlooked is that one usually meets the candidates and may have opportunities to influence them on issues and legislation of importance to all Differently Abled persons. One must also be able to face disappointments, however, because for every victory party there's a wake on the other side of town or the state. My first experience in politics was backing George McGovern, a debacle that disillusioned me for a few years, but since then I've helped make my doctor a Michigan senator and worked on lots of local campaigns.

The point of all this is that the more we're in circulation, the more men we will meet, some of whom are likely to be mature individuals who can appreciate the valuable things we wish to share. Even if we don't meet the man of our dreams right away, we will, undoubtedly, develop lots of good friends with whom to spend spare time, of which there won't be so much left anyway. For sure, it may be tougher for Differently Abled women to initiate and maintain relationships, but it can be done, as we have already seen and will continue to see in the coming pages.

7
Not a Helper
But a Helpmate
(Marriage)

Although marriage is but one of many types of relationships one might share with a partner in today's world, it can, and should be, I feel, the deepest and most profound. Therefore, I am devoting a separate chapter to the partnership of marriage. At the time they responded, twenty-four women were married. Fourteen others had been but were either separated, divorced, or widowed.

Attitudes toward marriage are changing. The following quotes reflect some of these changes: Rebecca Burns declared, "*Twenty years ago, I felt I had to be married and wouldn't have thought about having sex outside of marriage, and now I couldn't care less whether I'm married or not.*" Anet revealed that she is "*very uncomfortable in my role as wife. I've adopted political attitudes about the contract of marriage which put me in a very anti position. I don't like being married, and I don't like the way people regard me when I'm introduced as a wife. I ask (my husband) to introduce me as Anet _____ and let people figure out if I'm a friend, a sister or whatever....I think we're as close as star-crossed lovers could be, and I hardly see anything that could threaten that relationship so I don't mind being his wife in private. I just don't like being his wife in public.*"

Twenty-two women were married after they had become Differently Abled. Nineteen of these felt that even during courtship their mates were comfortable with their specific physical condition. Three had to adapt. Anet reported that her husband "*had to adapt to the idea that his woman wasn't perfect, but he added that no woman would have been perfect.*" Charlene, who was divorced, felt that, at first, her fiance had been "*demanding*" of her. Pooh Grayson needed her "*mate's assistance getting me in and out of cars, on and off curbs and steps, prepare food, give me drinks, place things within my reach. Our comfort level has generally changed for the better as we have gained knowledge about what I can and cannot do with him. Our comfort level also changes with our moods—how sensitive we are about my disability at the moment.*"

Reactions of family and friends to their marriages were inclined to be positive even if, occasionally, cautiously so. Fourteen respondents felt the feedback from those closest to them to be positive. Sally Smith stated, "*Everyone was happy when I found someone I could really love and vice versa.*" Jennifer felt that, prior to her marriage, family and friends were "*very cautious— asked more questions about finances and real love and commitment than other people would,*" adding, "*when I was married, I lived near to my husband's family, and they were quite kind and helped out with the different chores and things.*"

Nine received negative reactions. Brillig said, "*One aunt referred to him as my 'noble' husband. My mother told me it was the only marriage she'd help me with.*"

Five gauged the reactions as neutral or mixed. Julia's family "*thought it was really fantastic. His family had doubts until they got to know me and realized I could function effectively as a wife and homemaker.*" Marie R. reported, "*My mother didn't want me to get married so soon after my injury. The rest of my family and friends were happy. My husband's family didn't want him to marry me ever because of my disability.*"

Also mixed were community reactions.

Eight perceived opinions to be negative. Daisy D. "*was bitter because neighbor adults openly spoke ill of anyone interested in me. I had two lengthy serious romances before meeting my first husband. Gossippers said, 'Well, he had to marry her'....When no baby appeared, they said, 'Well, her mom's a nurse and aborted her.' I could not win.*" Marie R. recalled, "*I was never approached, but my parents were by some crusty people who wanted to advise* [them] *against me getting married.*" Shirley O'Hara said of her first wedding, "*They were aghast....I had a lot of uninvited guests....They wanted to see if I could walk up the aisle."* Brillig observed *"pity for my husband. Adulterous offers. Seemed to feel I was taking advantage of him."*

Six observed mixed reactions. Jennifer said that people were *"kind of shocked, especially other girlfriends that didn't have lovers. Close friends were delighted."* Editor of a newspaper for the Differently Abled, Nora Ellen noticed that the universal question was *"Is he handicapped too?"* (He wasn't.)

Nine felt community opinion to be mostly positive. Midge, a widow at the time of her response, remarked, *"I never noticed so I guess it was accepted."*

Only eight women were either currently or had been married to Differently Abled men. Annette, a widow, and Mrs. Lewis, a divorcee, both post-polios, had been married to men who also had polio. The others' spouses possessed different specific physical conditions such as hearing impairment or emotional disturbance. Sally Smith, whose husband has severe arthritis, said, *"...we live in a senior citizen's...housing development....My husband and I are the only two who are not elderly—we are in here because of our disabilities—both my husband and I are in wheelchairs....It's an unusual situation, we are an unusual couple, and so we have, I guess you could say, an unusual life."*

Marie R. expressed some universal concerns of Differently Abled married women: *"Being disabled also concerns me as a wife and mother. As a disabled wife, I want my husband happy with how I run our home and handle our children. And as a sexual being, I want my husband happy and satisfied in our relationship with each other. As a mother, I want my children comfortable about my handicap and to find no embarrassment in calling me their mother. I do not want my handicap to be their handicap and have it hold them back from any opportunity to enjoy a full life."*

Joan C., a housewife/teacher in her middle fifties, revealed that her present concern in regard to herself *"as a sexual being and a disabled woman are two-fold. Number one: That I might be able to continue physically, have the stamina to be able to maintain the degree of sexuality and sexual expression that I have had, and I mean by that, of course,...actual sexual intercourse with my partner...particularly since my partner is an extremely active and able person. We have been involved in therapy, and this has been extremely helpful in developing communication between us and opening inroads which we did not have in our early years, and perhaps this is, in a way, enabling us to maintain the level of sexuality or sexual expression that we have been able to do."*

"The second part...," she continued, *"relates to the fact that I*

am increasingly aware of the possibility of being left without a
sexual partner, should anything happen to my mate. This could
happen—it does happen all the time. I realize that, as a disabled
woman, I would possibly have a little more difficulty attracting a
sexual partner."

Adapting to a partner's physical condition that is constantly
changing presents a different set of concerns for both the Differently
Abled woman and her partner. Michelle, who became Differently
Abled after she was married, said, "*I have multiple sclerosis,
which means my physical condition is always changing....Prob-
ably my concern is that I will not want sex at all and worry over
how that will affect marriage, no matter how sympathetic my
husband is and how flexible we are (and have been for years)
about extramarital sex. For most things—and possibly at some
point in time—my husband and I can and do talk. But talk
doesn't fix everything....It is very scary to be constantly changing
in capabilities, and both of us feel that.*"

Although not "*officially married,*" Dahtee gave a poignant account of the stresses she and her partner encountered when she
became Differently Abled: "*L. and I began this intense relationship. We were dynamite in bed together, and fascinated with the
people that we were...for the first time, I was really going to get
my life together,...then the disease really began to set in for the
first time really noticeable—I mean I had a stiff knee when I first
met L....I was dating L. when it went up into my hip,...then, it
was only within the next couple of months that the pain became
generalized into almost every major joint in my body...and
fevers and weakness. And L. was very supportive,...through this
beginning state—anybody would be supportive of anybody they
loved in the beginning stages of problems like this....*

"*I guess it was four months into our relationship, they came
up with the diagnosis that it was rheumatoid arthritis, and by
this time I was living with L., and we went through this whole
thing of, if it does become progressive, as it was doing at the
time,...'Can we deal with the problem of my being in a
wheelchair?...' The initial result was, 'Of course, we can handle
this.' And then, all of a sudden, I was in the wheelchair, and we
weren't handling it....*

"*About six months into our relationship, they changed the
diagnosis into systemic lupus....So, during this time between the
two diagnoses, we were trying to work it out if we could live
together and make it with me disabled....There would be times
when I would get tired early....He didn't like it—had trouble with*

it—but one of the problems we faced was sex. There were nights when it was just too painful...even the weight of the sheets on my legs was excruciating...so, of course,....I wasn't interested in receiving sex....I wasn't interested in giving sex....It was very close to the end, and I remember his saying to me, 'Well, if you can't supply it, then I'm going to go out and get it.'

"And I said, 'Well, I don't know how I feel about that. Half of me wants to support you, is saying, 'Well, of course, you're a young man, you need it, go out and get it'; and the other half of me is saying, 'That's not fair, you take me, you take what I can or can't do, and there are times when I am capable of sex, y'know.'

"Shortly after that, L. came home and said, 'I can't love a cripple!' He was very angry—he was crying, and I was crying—and he was a little bit drunk so he screamed that out and just amazing amounts of pain and bitterness....We kept trying for months after that,...living apart, living together, living apart, living together, not knowing what we were going to do, and by that time, the disease progressed to the point where I was in and out of the wheelchair...so that we would have to readjust almost every time....Finally, he took off with a woman and went to South America."

Although we don't know the full circumstances of Dahtee's relationship with L., it is likely that both could have benefited from joint counseling. According to Vargo in his article entitled "The Disabled Wife and Mother: Suggested Goals for Family Counseling" (1979, pp. 108-111), this is especially important in situations where the specific physical condition may be hidden (epilepsy or cardiac conditions, for example) or may be frequently changing, as in Dahtee's case. When the limitations are not obvious and clear-cut, there is apt to be role ambiguity for both the Differently Abled individual and those closest to her. Although the earlier mistaken diagnosis made things more difficult, it would have been helpful for both partners to have been fully informed of Dahtee's physical condition as it changed, with ample time for questions and discussion as well as expectations for the future. This is particularly essential when the physical condition may cause personality changes beyond those involved in adjusting to the new limitations, such as the sudden mood swings associated with multiple sclerosis.

In an *Accent on Living* article on divorce, Robert T. Baxter says that marriages are much less likely to survive when the female suffers trauma than when the male does (Fall, 1981, pp. 49-50). Since the wife's role is so central to the whole family structure, this situation would probably place a great strain on the marriage.

Sixteen respondents became Differently Abled after they were married. Some of these marriages did not survive.

"*He divorced me,*" stated Jane K., an Indiana schoolteacher, "*He could not stand to be around me, and the idea of sex with me completely turned him off.*" A mother of three, Jane Grant, echoed, "*My ex-husband, I do not feel, could handle a disabled wife; therefore, I went through a bitter divorce.*" Bernice said her husband didn't "*accept* [her] *as a woman anymore.*" (They later separated.) Marta Lin, a fifty-seven-year-old Iowa housewife, said, "*He feels his need for sexual release should be taken care of, and I should have no needs—this is a false assumption! He finds it difficult to maintain erection because of my lack of physical activity in act. This hurts me....He goes to other women, but professes his complete love for me.*" Jennifer noted that as her condition progressed she was "*left in the car more...and left out of some activities because of the bother of lifting and wheelchair.*"

Vargo (op. cit., p. 110) reports that the meager research that has been done does not show a clear correlation between a spouse becoming suddenly Differently Abled and the dissolution of the marriage; however, if a separation or divorce does occur, it usually happens soon after the onset of the specific physical condition. Apparently, if the partners are able to survive the initial shock, they are likely to be able to make the adjustments necessary to the specific physical condition, a prerequisite for maintaining the marriage relationship in any kind of healthy, satisfying manner.

In a study of thirty-six Differently Abled married women between the ages of twenty-one and sixty, Skipper, et al. (1968, p. 17) found that there was a low correlation between the degree of physical mobility and the satisfaction of marital needs such as love, belonging, mutual esteem, sex, etc. Furthermore, only one woman was not participating in sexual relations with her husband because of problems connected with her specific physical condition (Ibid., p. 18).

I'm happy to report that my study, too, shows that most of my respondents and their mates have been able to weather the crisis. The following quotes illustrate some of the steps in their processes of adjustment.

Pamela, a polio quad, explained, "*We loved each other, but our whole world crumbled, and we had to rebuild.*" She went on to tell how their marriage had been improved and strengthened by "*constant love, giving, and trying to cope and understand what he needed; being independent—taking responsibility off his shoulders; accepting what he was and not fitting him into my mold of what he should be. Many times I've failed, but life is a constant challenge to cope, learn, improve oneself. With three children, a busy husband and household, there's never a dull moment."* Despite the problems triggered by her specific condition that she and her husband have yet to work out, Mae Evans also recorded a positive change in her marriage. *"He is more noticing of me, expresses kindness, shows his love, where before he sort of took me for granted—he loved me but never said so. His attitude did not change, he just got able to let me know daily how he feels." "At first, he did everything,"* Samantha remembered, *"after he realized I should be doing things for myself, he pushed me out of the nest."*

Marie R., who described her relationship with her husband as *"a perfect love triangle with the Lord,"* offered wise advice for making the adjustments and sacrifices necessary for achieving a happy marriage, whether or not one of the partners is Differently Abled: *"A marriage is not a fifty-fifty situation because then the husband and wife are only giving half to their marriage. It should be one hundred-one hundred all the way....There would be a lot less divorce if people would change their arithmetic in the numerical equation on marriage. With both partners giving 100%, there would be no needs left unfilled...this is hard to do in our lives, but with God's help we can come closer to a more perfect marriage."* Hopefully, as we learn to better know ourselves, each other, and God, more of us will attain this desirable state.

Hormones Know No Handicap
(Sexual Feelings)

Our sexuality is with us from the moment we're born. Not just in the fact of being born female or male and being treated accordingly, it influences to a great extent the way we view ourselves and the world around us. It is an integral part of our personhood.

Individual sexuality can be expressed in many ways at any age. Jennifer recalled, *"when I was in the hospital, and I was quite young, and I couldn't hardly move at all, and I was wiggling my toes to some rock-and-roll music one time,...the doctor came by and, after his visit, kind of played with my toes, and it just—it was a good feeling, having someone touch me."* Ebony, a nineteen-year-old Afro-Americna quadriplegic who, at the time of our interview, was about to have a baby, *"was dancing in the bed, to my abilities, and singing at the same time, and M. turned around and caught me and started laughing, and, you know, I thought he was just making fun of me, and he wasn't....I just really felt dumb."*

Ebony's self-consciousness in front of her boyfriend is a prime example of how society has conditioned us to negate our own sexuality. Anet said, *"I think some people feel I have no right to sexuality."* Patricia Maher also spoke of this denial of our personhood: *"The general public is not aware that handicapped people (women) are sexual beings and can be sexually satisfied...like handicapped people are not thought of as people. I've talked to classes or just people in general to point out that I do have so-called 'normal' sexual feelings and try to make people comfortable with the idea. More of this should be done."*

I agree that it must be done and frequently talk to classes here at the University of Michigan. Each time I do, however, I get angry—angry at a society that makes these talks essential and angry at their invasion of both my time and my privacy. But I will continue to do it because is is **so** necessary.

Jenny Jones pointed out, *"I don't think there's very much information around on it (sexuality), or if it is, it's tucked 'way away....It seems to be out in the open for most other groups except for the disabled...even in the movies they have so little about it; it's so, so much in evidence in every other field—every other type of sexual possibility except that."* Poodle Gal, mother of a fourteen-year-old daughter, emphasized, *"I think people should be told by newspapers or magazine articles, etc.,...that just because we are handicapped we are not incapable of sexual yearning and desires!"*

Being able to express one's sexuality in a free and normal way requires a degree of acceptance, and not just the acceptance of society or even that of the *"significant other"*, although this is important. Ultimately more important to our development as sexual beings is a true acceptance of ourselves—our complete selves—the good and the bad as well as the potential of our minds and spirits, instead of dwelling on the limitations of our specific physical conditions. Confirming this is Sandy Mitchell, who said, *"A large part of feeling good about myself has been due to really accepting my disability."*

Concentrating on the negatives about ourselves inhibits our openness to new feelings, people and situations. Lola said, *"I'm somewhat uncomfortable having sex with a man for the first time beause I'm unsure how he'll react to what polio did to my figure (no **Playboy** centerfold)."* I'm sure Lola's discomfort at those times has blocked a good deal of her spontaneous sensual enjoyment of the moment. I'm not surpirsed though that she added, *"The men I've known have been remarkably reassuring."* Very often we emphasize our problems much more than others do. Polio has given me a very pronounced spinal curvature, and I didn't think there was anything about my body appearance that could be considered aesthetically pleasing by anybody. Then, one day last summer, my lover came home from his brother's place and announced, *"I saw an ass in this month's **Playboy** that looks just like yours."* Flabbergasted, I insisted on going right out to buy one. Well, much as I can see of my backside, there did, surprisingly, seem to be a resemblance, which was later confirmed by a helper.

Daisy D. spoke also of her lack of self-acceptance: "*In my head, sometimes when things went wrong, I wondered if he missed arms around him or positions requiring knee bending, squatting, etc. Asked him point blank—he reassured me our problems were not stemming from my defects....But sometimes I chose to hurt myself by secretly feeling this...stroking and kissing the deformed parts, as well as the 'normal' parts, proved his acceptance of the total me.*" It's so easy to blame every difficulty on our specific physical condition when, in truth, there could be any number of factors, emotional, psychological, and/or physical, in either or both partners that can contribute to problems in a relationship.

When asked whether or not their current sex life was satisfying, the answers were almost evenly divided with thirty-six women saying that it was and thirty-seven saying that it wasn't. As might be suspected from reading thus far, the major reason cited for it being unsatisfactory was the lack of a willing partner (31).

The next highest numbers of reasons mentioned were medical problems (10), fear of physical discomfort (9), embarrassment about appliances, deformity, etc. (9), and religious or moral convictions (9). It is with the first three of these that we need be especially concerned, for probably the number of women indicating abstention from sexual activity because of religious or moral convictions would parallel those in the able-bodied population abstaining for the same reasons.

Mae Evans discussed the changes in her sexuality as a result of her spinal cord injury, "*Before paraplegia, I had confidence in bed. My husband desired me. It was all so easy and so automatic and fun, knowing I had this femininity that attracted him, and I used it. It's so different now. My body is racked with terrible burning pain all the time so most of the time I simply don't want sex. But sometimes I do long for it, I really want a good lay. I wish I could stop wanting it, but how do you stop wanting something that was so good? When we are together, I imagine what it used to feel like, and I concentrate on what I am doing to him,...then I think about me and a lot of times end up crying which does not help any.*"

Perhaps the worst inhibitor to the free expression of one's sexuality is fear because of ignorance about sexual feelings and processes. Jay Kirfirst confided *"the greatest fear of ever having to be in such a situation with a man. Any man. Why I have this fear I do not know really except that it is REAL and more fearful to me than death and I am not lying...maybe it is the fear of a not perfect body, of having embarrassing things happen by the excitement, etc., or just the fear of not knowing what to do, and, perhaps, being laughed at for this. I can't really explain it even to myself, but the relationship I recently had by mail made me physically ill to think that it was to have gone on to other areas. He knew this but assured me we could work out whatever we had to physically and otherwise, but I don't think he fully understood how I felt....Never in my life before these two-and-a-half years, did I even consider such a situation, and God only knows how I had to force myself to try and accept that it might really happen. The fears were with me always. And still are though I doubt I'll ever have to think about such areas again."*

"My present concerns are virtually limitless," said Connie L., *"Fear that he will be repulsed by my body. Gynecological problems of various sorts, probably all of little importance and quite natural but which have taken on monstrous proportions in my mind after all the years of never discussing this sort of thing with a doctor. Fear that I am sure to be deformed in some way internally which would interfere with my being able to have sex, because after all, why should that part of my body be any different than the rest? Feelings of inadequacy and embarrassment at my lack of experience. Fear that I wouldn't be able to reach orgasm in any manner, again, because my body, not sex, is bad. Doubts about being able to handle the emotional demands of a sexual relationship. Fear of disease in the genital area. Just in general feeling that sex is too good, in some sense, for me."*

Illustrating the difference a little knowledge and reassurance can make in comfort and confidence about one's sexuality are two quotes from Deena. In the first questionnaire, she was worried about being able to function sexually, saying, *"I'm scared—I don't know what to do or how to do it."* By the time she replied to the follow-up survey, everything had changed, largely because her doctor had taken the time to show her the inside of her vagina. She almost bubbled, *"I was...able to do something I wanted so much to do but was so scared of. I am talking about intercourse. I now feel like a whole sexually adult woman."*

Rebecca Burns described her self-help techniques to reassure herself that she was sexually functional: *"I just couldn't imagine how the vagina could stretch to make intercourse possible, and it's been a phobia. I felt that I was hopelessly tight. After I had had this operation (hysterectomy), I had heard a lot about what happens to women if they don't...secrete estrogen and don't take estrogen replacement...they develop what is called vaginal atrophy. I was very upset about this. I made up my mind to take estrogens temporarily and during those few months would stretch myself...while I still had the potential to be elastic. I used vibrators, beginning with one about three-quarter inch in diameter, and the next one, one-and-one-quarter inch and the final one, over a period of about three months, one-and-one half inches and stretched myself. I broke most or all of my hymen and bled a little. There was some discomfort but no pain....*

"*This has been extremely gratifying for me,*" she continued, "*it removed this whole fear because now I know how my body works. I know how my vagina can relax and gradually expand to accommodate any size. And this is what I had to...prove to myself. It was part of my self-esteem. I am going to continue these stretching exercises at least twice a week indefinitely....I know I'm a normal woman. That's very important to me. My fears were very foolish, but they were there, and I'm free of them now.*"

Other reasons mentioned for an unsatisfactory sex life were lack of privacy (7) and negative sanction by parents or attendants (4).

Because Differently Abled women are often taught to ignore their bodies and concentrate on the development of their minds, the sensual aspects of sex may be especially important. Pooh Grayson related, "*I enjoy sex because I can be successful in a physical way to the mutual satisfaction of myself and my partner.*" I, too, feel very good when I am able to give another physical pleasure. Being almost always the receiver of so many physical ministrations from attendants and others, it is great to give to another in such a special way. Also the motion and friction against my body which occur in lovemaking improve my circulation, (normally bad), making me feel all warm and rosy, so I receive an extra bonus too.

Larkin discussed a different aspect. "*I don't really desire intercourse especially. I want to experience many things in the world, but I don't feel it is a higher priority than riding a motorcycle, going to Europe, etc. I **do** desire touch, hugging, etc., and am learning to express that need and to give it. In my opinion, 'fucking' is greatly overestimated in this culture. Confusion between these two needs is the main source of embarrassment or discom-*

fort." Then, she gave some examples of feelings important to her: "*tenderness for someone or a need in myself to be connected (I call it a 'grounding wire') to the world. Sometimes it was scary in New Orleans, me and D. alone in a new city—while she was at work, I was on my own for eight hours—I met a lot of well-meaning uncoordinated people. When M. carried me up a flight of stairs, I nearly fainted with relief. Every movement was thought out and coordinated. No fuck could have been so physically satisfying as M.'s lift up the stairs each night. I desired and depended on that moment of physical security each night.*"

"*Closeness with another person is a big part of the kick in sex,*" for Laura. Summer agreed, "*I would rather be held.*" The longing for touching, caressing and massage, listed as preferred turn-ons by twenty-six women, is not unique to Differently Abled women. Ashley Montagu, in his book, **Touching**, (1972, pp. 188-9) speaks of a study of thirty-nine able-bodied women done by Dr. Marc H. Hollender, in which over half (21) had used sex in order to be held and twenty-six had made direct requests to be held. Author of a new book called **Nice Girls Do**, Dr. Irene Kassorla, in an interview with **People Magazine**, (Kalter, 1981) more recently stated, "*Other than being fed, being held and touched is probably the most significant interaction that produces the sense of security and comfort.*" Her male patients admitted to often using intercourse as a means of being held and caressed, a ruse usually only attributed to women. They feared that merely requesting it would be considered unmasculine.

For our purposes, it may be even more significant that ten of our twenty-six respondents favoring tactile stimulation had become Differently Abled either at birth or during the first five years of life. For a number of reasons, Differently Abled children often do not receive the same amount of holding and cuddling as able-bodied children. Their specific condition may make it physically difficult or uncomfortable for either the parents or the child. The sheer amount of time and energy required just to provide for her bodily needs may preclude this kind of playfulness which, although essential to a child's emotional growth, may be regarded as frivolous by the parents. They may be also incapable of demonstrating physical affection to the child because of their own guilt and frustration (see Chapter Four).

Montagu quotes Anna Freud (op. cit., pp. 187-8) on the importance of affection and cuddling in childhood to adult sexual adjustment: "*At the beginning of life...being stroked, cuddled, and soothed by touch libidinizes the various parts of the child's body, helps to build up a healthy body image...and simultaneously promotes the development of object love by cementing the bond bet-*

ween child and mother. There is no doubt that, at this period, the surface of the skin in its role as erotogenic zone fulfills a multiple function in the child's growth." Montagu, himself, commented, *"The mother's holding and cuddling of the child plays a very effective and important role in its subsequent sexual development. A mother who loves must enfold the child she loves. She must draw the child to her in a close embrace and, male or female, this is what the adult will want later and be able to demonstrate to anyone he loves."*

Kassorla and Montagu disagree on what effects might be expected in adults who have not received this maternal nurturance as children. Both viewpoints are supported by my study.

Kassorla found that adults who had been so deprived shunned touching relationships and often experienced sexual difficulties. Recall the problems in initiating and maintaining sexual relationships mentioned by Mary James, Jay Kirfirst and Connie L.

Montagu felt that this early deprivation often resulted in excessive craving for caresses as adults and he cites prostitutes as often having suffered a lack of fondling as children. I grew up with almost no physical touching except when things were done for me, and I chronically crave being held and caressed. In my younger years, I used sex to receive affection, but now I am becoming more open in communicating what I really do need. Since I have been more honest about my needs, I've found men are often relieved because that's what they have wanted too. As we become more open about ourselves, it frees them to be more honest, too.

Larkin gave some examples of non-sexual touching in her life: *"Parents when I was small; a whole summer rolling about our living room floor with a female friend when I was nineteen; 'tequila nights' at our commune-like house where we all were high and lay in a tangle on the floor; hugging and holding;...spending hours in a bathtub in New Orleans with a woman friend, tracing maps of the city on each other's back...; on nights I am lonely or fearful, asking one of the persons in my house to hold me."*

Seven women preferred romantic settings or expectations of them as their favorite turn-ons. Penny S. wanted *"candlelight, or a dark room with the curtains half-open. My lover looking into my eyes, touching my face, holding my hands."* Samantha said, *"When some outside stimuli arouses me when partner is absent, I set the stage (remove child from scene, prepare food, bed, self)*

101

for lovemaking and fantasize what will be said and done when partner returns." Beth, who became a paraplegic at the age of eleven, said her favorite turn-ons were *"touch, candles, a drink, doing things together, having a good day together and feeling close, taking a shower together and making love."*

Audio-visual effects were favored by some. Lola preferred *"a man with an attractive body, a nice cock; porno movies; certain types of music; his moans or mine; a man who's really turned on with me (probably related to my insecurity); a man telling me in detail what he wants to do with me sexually."* Martha Merriweather was especially aroused by *"erotic literature."* Tommi, whose Grissell's syndrome began at the age of three, said, *"A handsome man or romantic books or movies."* Julia's favorite stimuli were *"reading adult literature, talking with my husband about sex, getting spanked by my husband,...mutual masturbation, ...vibrator, oral sex, other men showing interest in me."* April listed, *"Music, intellectually stimulating conversation, chocolate skin, hair brushing against me."* Nora Ellen, a thirty-six-year-old Canadian social worker and editor, had an unusual visual turn-on, *"A view of a man's balls from the rear and slightly below."*

Seven women listed manipulation of the clitoris and fondling of their breasts as their best sexual stimuli. Helen Beach, a paraplegic, said that her most sensitive areas were *"back of neck, face, deep tongue kissing, nipples, armpits, hyperesthesia around level of injury, caressing my back. Plus, I find it stimulating visually to watch sexual activity."*

Reactions of partners were very important to three women. Michelle said, *"Partner's turn-on has a big effect on me."* Brillig elaborated further, *"Unexpected glimpses or awareness of sexuality, non-hostile male bahavior, feeling of having personally created a good thing."*

Oral sex was the favorite turn-on of three women. Colleen Moore apparently meant fellatio when she said, *"the knowledge I'm in control; the feeling I'm desired, appreciated....I also love oral sex, and most men (all?) really respond."* Helen W. specified, *"Oral sex—cunnilingus; mutual masturbation, physical contact. But the best turn-on occurs when I really like the guy—then everything is stimulating."*

Two women spoke of particular times they got especially aroused. Mrs. Lewis recalled, *"I used to get all turned on at the office between 1-3 p.m.—no, not the men around—I don't know why."* Patricia Maher noticed that her *"vagina muscles tighten up,...more often than not, it feels more relaxed and pleasurable in dreams (sleeping) than in reality."*

When asked how much of the time they were not really in the mood for love making, twenty-seven women reported that they were sometimes unlikely to be aroused. Fatigue was the reason most frequently cited by this group (16); followed by stress (6); attitudes of partners (3); pain (2); just plain not in the mood (2); too busy (1); constipation (1); and dislike of intercourse (1). As one can see by the figures, some women listed more than one reason for occasionally not being in the mood to be aroused.

Seven women were always in the mood to be aroused, and twenty-four said that they almost always were. The reasons the latter group gave for their rare lack of enthusiasm for sexual arousal were fatigue (6); stress (5); lack of sensation (1); the learning of self-control (1); fear (1); and just plain not in the mood (1). Perhaps because the disinterest occurred so seldom, this group was much less likely to label their infrequent lack of libido (15) as compared with thirty-two reasons mentioned by the first group.

Seven women were frequently not in the mood for sexual arousal. One respondent each cited unavailability of a partner, the attitude of her partner, stress, and infrequent ovulation.

Thirty women said they would like to be sexually aroused more frequently. Liz Williams specified *"by someone I care about."* Nine women wanted to be aroused less often while twenty-six were satisfied with the status quo.

When asked under what conditions they would be most likely to be aroused, nine women said with the right person. Patricia Maher loved *"men who are tender, loving, respecting, and gentle."* Five women specified *"when not tired,"* a figure I was surprised was not higher, considering that fatigue was such an important factor in the previous two questions. Kathryn, whose polio occurred when she was twenty-four, was most likely to be aroused *"when happy, relaxed and not uncomfortable with disability."*

Eight women were aroused most easily when there was sufficient time and privacy. Of these, three were mothers of children and two were students, groups who normally lack both. Four women found that being high, usually on alcohol, helped them to relax and become aroused more easily.

Three women said that they were most easily aroused around the times of their menstrual periods. Jennifer added, *"Around the middle of the month, probably during ovulation, I am aroused mostly automatically."* Three others noted that they were more turned on after a period of abstinence, and three respondents became most aroused after fantasizing.

Understandably, several of my respondents' fantasies were concerned with being able to move more than they are presently capable of during sexual activity and to satisfy their partners in ways they are now unable to do. These may correspond roughly to the "Life Can Be Beautiful" syndrome described by Nancy Friday in her book on women's sexual fantasies, **My Secret Garden** (1976), in which women fantasize that they are much more attractive than they are in reality. The fantasy of Marta Lin, a paraplegic, was "**to be able to satisfy my husband so he will need no outside help.**" Pooh Grayson, a polio quad, fantasized, "**Putting my arms around my partner by myself and touching him in ways I can't now because of my disability.**" Hot Wheels, a divorced paraplegic, dreamed of "**not being handicapped and feeling everything with a perfectly wonderful man.**" Jennifer, who has myasthenia gravis, specified, "**Someone helping me achieve orgasms, when I am capable, by other means than intercourse.**"

In thinking about my own night dreams and waking fantasies, I realized that in them I'm never Differently Abled at all, but, since I don't remember what it feels like to put one foot in front of the other, I just sort of float around like Peter Pan.

Nancy Friday discussed the following types of fantasies in a chapter entitled "Insatiability" in which she said that they did not necessarily represent a desire for more sex but were merely some of the avenues by which we "**can unravel the mystery of what it is to be and feel a woman**" (1976, p. 55). For example, fantasies involving multiple lovers were enjoyed by ten women. E. B. Browning, a polio quad, dreamed of "**riding down a highway with a Doberman (for protection, although she is very gentle except on command), picking up one or two hitchhikers (fellows) and going to a motel....I am (in my fantasy) a paraplegic.**" Sandy Mitchell favored, "**Stripping, usually in front of more than one person.**" Ursula, a thirty-one-year-old student, craved "**being made love to alternately by two different men.**" Scarlett, true to her name, wanted "**sexual encounters with a variety of men.**" Martha Merriweather was a little more specific: "**Being in bed with two men at once—one para and one walker.**" Jane Smith, who uses a wheelchair because of rheumatoid arthritis, fantasized about "**taking part in a wild orgy and being made love to and making love to many people; watching my husband get aroused by having two beautiful women lick and suck his penis.**" April wished for "**two or three men making love to me at once, one sucking my nipples, the second on my clitoris, another fucking me.**" Rebecca Burns imagined herself "**a virgin forced to submit to** *a group orgy. I become wildly aroused against my will, become 'addicted' and come back begging for more."*

She continued, *"I am unable to contemplate sex without any kind of emotional involvement, unable to think of advertising for a male sex partner, unable to go to a sex therapist for sex or to a massage parlor....Yet, in my erotic fantasy world, I do things like that. What I crave most is a man's hand on my breast and to have my nipple sucked with his fingers up my vagina."*

Larkin had an interesting fantasy, a little like the Earth Mother type described by Friday: *"As a child, I used to fantasize two men holding and loving each other. I took turns identifying with either role. I guess, at that time, women did not even exist in my fantasy world. I could see nothing appealing about being a woman. Now I'm either a man or a woman...sometimes a group. The people involved are holding, hugging, falling asleep, closing the day together. And I fantasize us taking turns being children small enough to cuddle and swing through the air. I fantasize dancing."*

A favorite sensual fantasy of mine is that I am a yellow daffodil, one among many, swaying in the breeze in the middle of a big field. The air is warm on my face, and the sky is blue and cloudless. A group of nature study people come tramping by. They stop to discuss us but don't pick any and soon walk on. Then, I see J. strolling through the field. When he gets to me, he squats down and cups my face gently between his hands, his long slender fingers curving around me like a whisper. He puts his nose down to smell me. Then he picks me and slips me into his shirt pocket. Standing up, he puts his hands in his pants pockets and lopes across the field. I feel so warm and secure, jostling along next to his heart beating softly against me.

Being dominated was a popular fantasy for eight women. Abdication of responsibility is the important factor here. By being **forced** to do things one has been taught are *"**not nice**,"* one can avoid the guilt involved in consciously making the decision to do them and still enjoy them. Rebecca Burns, who appeared to have a rich fantasy life, said, *"Always with a stranger or a manipulative, tantalizing, and dominating type (no love or personal feeling at all)....I'm a child of thirteen being initiated by a 'dirty old man'."* Shirley O'Hara fantasized *"being raped—or forced—not in a life or death manner, but by someone who just has to take me, someone who has a large penis and who wishes to impregnate me."* Colleen Moore dreamed of *"having the undivided attention of a powerful man."* Rather than a stranger, Jane Grant said, *"Having my man* simply *'take me' and be a bit rough, saying to me, 'You're mine'.*" Julia had two favorite fantasies: the first, "*Being bad (or pretending I've been bad) and getting my fanny spanked;*" the second, "*Having someone so turned on to me that he tries everything outside of rape to get me in the sack, including vulgar language and lavish promises and force.*" Summer gave us this fantasy: "*To be tied and to have someone smother me with kisses, licks, touches and then to perform oral sex on me until I can't orgasm anymore—preferably it would be with someone I care for, and there would be a huge mirror above us. I'm a little apprehensive because I would be so vulnerable, but I think it would help me to be more secure with myself as a sexual being.*"

Three women had exhibitionistic fantasies. As well as the domination/submission component, Marlene C., a thirty-five-year-old post-polio from Arkansas, displayed this tendency: "*Being raped or forced to submit to intercourse, often in public, or at least around people.*" Carol Sea also fantasized that "*someone is watching.*" A little different version of exhibitionism was mentioned by Jessica, "*Someone first talks to me about what he is going to do in varying positions and then does it.*"

I tend to be somewhat exhibitionistic myself, and, at least in my own case, I feel that it stems from a wish for people to know that I am a sexual being. Subconsciously, I, and perhaps others, think that if society could see me doing something overtly sexual, there would be no further possibility of my being treated as a helpless eunuch.

Three women dreamed of oral sex. Lola fantasized "*A man performing cunnilingus on me; having two men at once (front and back); watching two men make it.*"

Romantic settings and/or eternal love, by far the most popular fantasy, were conjured up by fifteen women. Nancy said, "*I often fantasize about being on an island. My partner is someone whom I'm involved with sexually and emotionally. Only two of us there. We have our music, books and food, but no responsibilities. No restrictions on behavior, no clothes required.*" Helen W. preferred, "*being at a secluded villa in the mountains. Swimming nude, making love out in the warm sun. Having breakfast at an intimate café. Taking out a small luxury yacht, swimming, making love on the boat, rocking with the waves.*" Mary Jones, a North Carolina college student, wanted, "*just to lie in a warm room with him, no covers, no clothes, nothing to do; completely satisfied with everything.*" Joan C., mother of two teenagers, fantasized about "*having sex on the living room floor before an open fire.*" Owen dreamed of, "*having a man, one man in particular, love me in every way. Making gentle love to me, exploring every part of my mind and body.*" Liz Williams specified, "*Waking up in the arms of someone I care about.*" Woodie wished "*to take a bath with my partner and then make love afterwards.*"

There were a few unique fantasies. Patricia Maher dreamed of "*going to bed with Elvis Presley.*" Pooh Grayson fantasized "*that I am a super good lover and I really turn my partner on.*" There was an androgynous tone to Penny S.'s fantasy, "*A handsome man or woman slowly undressing me and then we have really fantastic sex together.*"

One interesting contrast between my respondents and those of Nancy Friday is that she indicated that many women were not interested in having their fantasies become reality (Ibid. p. 55) whereas thirty-nine of my respondents said that they **would** really like to do what they had described in their fantasies.

Six women said that they definitely would not want to live out their fantasies, and five women each said that maybe they would like to act them out but were undecided. Those who had some misgivings about their fantasies becoming reality were usually those whose dreams had included rape, multiple partners, or some form of exhibitionism.

My respondents' fantasies were remarkably similar to those recorded by Nancy Friday (1975, 1976). As I have always maintained, whether or not we are Differently Abled, our minds are free, and we have the same interests, desires, appetites and dreams as all women. Even the women who fantasized their specific physical condition to be less inconvenient were not much different from those who, in fantasy, were taller, slimmer, more buxom, or otherwise more physically attractive than they were in reality. I do not feel that either study shows any particular denial of the situational reality but merely enhances it, like adding a little extra perfume or make-up for special evenings.

The seven women who did not have sexual fantasies are also normal. Mary James exclaimed, "*I don't think I have one! God, am I abnormal or something?*" No. Many women do not use their imaginations this way. Collette, a twenty-eight-year-old housewife who has Fredrich's ataxia, said, "*I don't really have one, but I don't feel I'm lacking because of it.*" Michelle also had "*very little fantasy life—think of movies, photos I've seen sometimes. Think of past intense experiences.*"

Their reasons varied. One can almost see Mae Evans smile as she said, "**Don't fantasize, believe it or not! My husband is the real thing.**" Linda didn't "**have sexual fantasies. I might have more inhibitions since the birth of my child, but I am not sure why.**"

As we have seen throughout this book, respondents' ignorance about both the anatomical and emotional aspects of their sexuality as well as society's denial of it are the two main obstacles to be overcome in order for us to function freely as the sexual beings we were all born to be.

9

For Pleasure or Progeny
(Sexual Intercourse)

Sexual enjoyment may occur in many ways—with a partner, male or female, alone in masturbation, with or without mechanical aids such as dildos or vibrators. It usually involves some type of contact with the genital organs although occasionally women have reported having orgasms while reading, listening to beautiful music, or tensing and relaxing their thigh muscles. This chapter will be mainly concerned with heterosexual intercourse.

Of my seventy-five respondents, twelve had never experienced sexual intercourse. Seven of these had had their specific physical conditions since birth, and two others had contracted theirs at the ages of one and two years: I wonder if their early socialization taught them to believe that sexual activity was not possible. What part did the attitudes of society play in preventing them from meeting suitable partners for sexual experimentation?

Rebecca Burns stressed the importance of disabled people having other options. Her "*only romantic physical contact occurred when I was forty-five. He visited me for a week. With no attendant except my mother and his sister, we remained in our wheelchairs. He has no feeling from the chest down. We kissed, petted, and he masturbated me. He showed me his penis, I experienced scarcely any embarrassment. The feeling of closeness, the loving understanding of each other's body defects, the trust and tenderness, the joy I felt from his touch,* *made it a peak experience in my life. I felt **no inhibition** with this, my first romantic date, but I was unable to reach an orgasm. I felt that he was waiting for me to come, and I felt great distress about disappointing him, hurting his pride as a lover."*

Sally Smith agreed on the importance of sexual options, for, although she had not experienced intercourse, she, nevertheless, enjoyed a satisfactory sex life. Her *"husband is disabled also (arthritis) and confined to a wheelchair. We have a positional problem—but do achieve satisfaction, and it gets better each time. At first, it bothered me a great deal, but now it doesn't as we both achieve satisfaction and we have a genuine love for each other. I've a super, super sensitive set of breasts, and I just about—ecstacy—when my husband fondles and plays with my breasts, and it's just heaven when he sucks on them so this is totally satisfying for me....I go in another world when he does this for me...and I work on B., I masturbate him, I guess you could say, and he has an orgasm....I do occasionally go down on him, perform oral sex—fellatio, I believe the word is—anyway he also enjoys this; so he has told me at different times."*

Experiencing sexual intercourse for the first time is frequently traumatic for able-bodied women. It is no less so for Differently Abled women. Forty-two respondents had their initial experience after the onset of their specific physical condition. Although embarrassment and self-consciousness may be expected in this situation, it seemed to be a more significant factor for them. Tommi, who uses a wheelchair because of Grissell's Syndrome, recorded embarrassment *"because of my wearing diapers and also the fact that I must be undressed as well as dressed. Positioning was also a problem for me and him. He was quite accepting considering all that had to be done before intercourse was to be attempted."* Poodle Gal remembered, *"The only feeling I had about being embarrassed was when the time had come to get undressed—and since I needed help—I hoped that the man I was with would sense this and help me without any weird feelings."* Simone, a twenty-two-year-old Illinois student, worried about *"how he would feel about me being an amputee. It did not bother him a bit."*

Because of ingorance, many women suffered unnecessary anxiety about whether or not they were capable of intercourse. Anet said, *"I wasn't sure I could 'do it' because of my disability. No one ever talked to me about whether my genitals were involved in my disability. I lost my virginity at age sixteen to a boy who wanted to marry me. We both felt quite proud of our accomplishment afterwards, though I, of course, didn't even know about orgasm.*" Mary Jones, a twenty-three-year-old paraplegic, said that the only reason she "*finally gave in was to see for myself I could. I was engaged to this guy, and he didn't really care too much about sex, he said, but I knew better. He was satisfied but I didn't feel anything different, but I didn't tell him. It didn't make any difference to me—I just wanted to satisfy him.*"

Several were apprehensive about being able to adequately satisfy their partners. Woodie "*didn't even know if I could even have sex at first, and, if so, I didn't think I would be good enough to satisfy him....I had a little trouble getting into position at first. I was a little embarrassed about it.*" Marlene C., whose polio occurred when she was seven, recalled, "*My partner was unable to maintain an erection, and I assumed it was because of my lack of physical/bodily attractiveness and not stimulating him through body movements. He was disabled himself in one leg but had dated non-disabled girls previously. My participation was pretty passive but adequate, although we did not complete intercourse (orgasm), and I believe it was my fault.*" Summer, who has amyotonia congenita, was also afraid that she "*would not be able to perform adequately to satisfy my partner....Because I have limited mobility, it was difficult to achieve insertion, and because I had no previous experience, I did not know how to tell him to move me to make things easier. Plus IT HURT! I felt very...insecure with myself as a woman and as a lover. I also was unhappy because my disability was the major problem, and there is really nothing I can do about that.*"

Occasionally, there are genuine complications that must be worked out in order for some Differently Abled women to fully participate in and enjoy intercourse. Summer's solution: "*Becoming more assertive about my partner's actions (telling what's most comfortable and how to move me) and experimenting with different positions such as rear entry makes this better sexually.*" For April, "*it took several painful unsuccessful tries before I found out that I had to lie on my stomach or side because of the tilt of my pelvis. This made me feel less than a woman, and I still feel badly about not being able to hold my partner close.*" Jennifer "*needed more time to complete the act, like three months instead of one night. Had to take it easy 'cause of pain and I was small. Kind of upset at first. Worried more if husband's parents found out, especially father-in-law, that I wasn't like a normal wife. Got over it O.K.*" Linda "*worried about complications because of my catheter. I was also afraid of becoming pregnant.*"

Julia, who is also spinal cord injured, elaborated, "*Although I had sex before I was disabled, the first time afterward was un-comfortable because I was afraid I would have to void during in-tercourse (and I did). My disabled peers also had experienced the same problem. We had some problem positioning my legs comfortably. I had to void too often (interruptions)....We went about overcoming this situation by experimenting with posi-tions. With time, my bladder quit giving me trouble during sex. At times, we use K-Y Jelly for extra lubrication."*

Sometimes, attitudes of partners can make our first experience with sexual intercourse more difficult. Penny S. related, *"My first sexual experience was with someone I met the same night. He helped me walk into his apartment building because he didn't want to push me in my chair."* Helen Beach discussed her initial experience: *"He was afraid he was going to hurt me at first. I didn't feel anything, and I cried. We went about overcoming this situation by talking, touching—I'd tell him what felt best and move him where I wanted him. We learned to experiment, found new erogenous zones and became much less genitally focused."*

Our own attitudes about being Differently Abled may be a factor too. Lola, sixteen-and-a-half the first time she had intercourse, *"felt self-conscious about no longer having a beautiful figure, a body I could be proud of and want to show off....Also, I worried about not being able to move my hips. I don't worry about that now because in many positions a woman doesn't move that much, and the men I've had sex with have assured me it's O.K. with them and have been more than willing 'to do all the work,' move in ways I like best, etc. Also, as a form of 'compensation' I've worked to develop a degree of strength and skill with my vaginal muscles. The men like it, and it increases my pleasure too....I take great pride in being 'tight'."*

Boyfriends were most likely to have been partners in these first ex-periences (32); followed by husbands (13); male friends other than boyfriends (6); camp counselor (1); family member (1); and rapist (1). Thirty-five women felt their partners' attitudes about them were generally positive, and only one felt his attitude was negative. Four women were unable to pinpoint the exact nature of their first partners' attitudes.

Eleven women felt that through experience, a touch of maturity, and open communication with their partners, they were able to solve most of their early difficulties involving intercourse. Pooh Grayson, in sharing how she and her partner arrived at a mutually beneficial arrangement, gave some excellent advice: *"let me give you an example of how to arrive at a satisfying sexual realtion-*

*ship. **Ask what your partner likes**—I get him to talk about specifics. If he likes to have his back kissed, then we figure out how to get into a position. Solution: he turns me on my side and lays down on his side in front of me, and I can kiss his back.*

*   **Tell your partner what you like**. I get more satisfaction with foreplay before sexual intercourse so I ask him to touch me on the breasts, tummy, or thighs.*

*   **Be willing to experiment**. Not everything will work. I can get on my side, my tummy and my back with help from my partner. I have had sex in all combinations of those positions. I have tried some sitting positions, but they haven't worked out. If you can't do something you try, fantasizing about it can help. Sex has something for everybody if you are willing to make the effort to find it."*

The need for patience is stressed by Woodie: *"I am very fortunate in having found my particular partner. He is very patient. He tries very hard to understand me, my needs. He understands my physical limitations even better than I do sometimes. I don't have any control over my bladder, and when I was ten years old they...surgically rerouted my bladder, and now I must wear a urinostomy bag....He even at times jokes about my urinostomy bag, which is very unusual, but he does it in a kidding way. It has never been a put-down.*

*   "Another thing that is important is to understand for both of the couple that not every time that you have sex is it going to be great. I mean you're going to have your good days and your bad days, that all can't be winners....It's something that just goes with the territory, especially when you have a non-disabled person, as in my case. It is extremely important for that person to know the physical limitations of the other one, especially where sex is concerned."*

For everyone, open, honest communication is the key to good sex, but for the Differently Abled, who may have unique inconveniences to be overcome, its necessity cannot be overemphasized. Pamela, whose polio occurred when she was twenty, said, *"My inability to move easily requires my husband to assume the responsibility of positioning. I have felt inadequate about this, but we have talked about it and now I feel comfortable (and so does he). We have also found a great deal of pleasure in pleasuring one another rather than intercourse."* Poodle Gal disclosed that she and her husband *"have been married fourteen-and-a-half years and we enjoy sex more now than when we were first married. But now it's the **quality** that counts! Not the quantity. I* *have always had a higher sex-drive than my husband and am slowly adjusting happily to his timetable."*

Understanding and good humor are certainly helpful in weathering the occasional inconveniences caused by a partner's specific condition which may occur during sex. *"One time I had blood in my urine following intercourse. I saw a doctor about it, and he said it could have resulted from intercourse but couldn't tell for sure. Once after prolonged intercourse,"* Linda recounted, *"my husband developed a slight pressure mark along the penis from my catheter. Once I had a bowel accident during intercourse. A couple of times my catheter has come out. In all cases, I was mortified, but they all happened....My husband is very understanding and doesn't seem to get discouraged. Most of the time everything works out satisfactorily."* Samantha, a mother of a seven-year-old daughter, stated, *"Originally I was much less mobile, more often tired—then, doc. pumped me full of Valium for muscle spasms. We did not know it was a tranquilizer, and I was not even aware we were not having sex....I cut down to two milligrams a day and have recently quit. I resent what that doc. did to me."* Helen Beach has found that *"if I forget to catheterize afterwards, I usually get a bladder infection."*

Although the book, **Sexual Options for Paraplegics and Quadriplegics** (Mooney et al., 1975) advises what to do with a catheter during intercourse, both the pictures and text are vague regarding women. However, I think their illustration of draping it up and across the hip would work just as well for women as men. To avoid putting too much pressure on the catheter and stopping the flow of urine, it would be wise to decide on what position will be used ahead of time, then tape the catheter in place so that it doesn't come between you and your partner. To reduce friction on your partner's penis from rubbing against the catheter, as described by Linda, the authors recommend using a lubricant, such as K-Y Jelly.

Again, we must remember that unpleasant incidents occasionally happen during sex to everyone, Differently Abled or not, and not unduly blame ourselves or our specific physical condition. My last lover (a t.a.b.) once had to stop in the middle of lovemaking to urinate, an unwelcome interruption, of course, but nothing more. Michelle, who has multiple sclerosis, had *"a fear of bowel/bladder control loss during numbness."* Obviously, as far as it is possible to schedule an activity such as intercourse that should occur spontaneously, it would be advisable to try to arrange it for times when bowels have been emptied for the day. I usually void before intercourse, not so much because I fear a bladder accident (although I recognize this as a very real possibility), but because the dual pressures from inside my vagina and outside on my stomach cause discomfort if my bladder is not empty.

Because we're not much different sexually from other people, as often as possible we should seek solutions to our problems that are seen as beneficial by the rest of the population. Illustrating this is Samantha: "*I could not move as I had before to achieve orgasm. I felt depressed but pretty stoic. Now we use a waterbed which magnifies any movements I can achieve.*"

Respondents have found some positions better suited for sexual intercourse than others. Woodie and her partner "*use two primary positions. One is modified woman superior...where I mount him, and I have my back to his face. The only problem with this particular position is you do not have the closeness. For instance, any cuddling, fondling, foreplay cannot take place, although there is a lot of that afterward and beforehand....I do have back problems, and because of this sometimes I have rather a lot of discomfort and pain in my back—I simply can't physically do that type of positioning. The other way where both of us are on our sides and he enters from the rear...the depth of penetration is not as intense as it is the other way although in this positioning we can touch each other, he can put his arms around me, fondle me, caress me while intercourse is taking place....I get pleasure both ways.*" For Dahtee, "*sex is usually when I'm lying on my side, and then the man would enter from the rear...or else like side to side where I'm lying on by back and only like across him—like he's lying with his head on the pillow and his feet to the bottom, for example, and I would by lying kitty-corner to him.*"

Jane Smith, who has rheumatoid arthritis, explained how she and her husband achieve sexual pleasure: "*As far as joint movements restricting me where sex positions are concerned, my knees are fused, and I walk stiff-legged, and when we have sex there are only a few things we can do with pleasure. It's hard for me to spread my legs apart. When I'm naked and lying on my back, my husband lies on top of me and can—with much effort—put his stiff penis inside my vagina. Usually, we just french-kiss for a while until he turns around and with his tongue licks and caresses my pubic hair and clitoris while I lick and suck his already hard and large penis. After I have an orgasm and before he comes in my mouth...he helps me onto my stomach. Then he puts two pillows under my hips to raise them and spreads my legs as far apart as they go...and puts his still*"

115

hard penis inside me and moves in an out until he comes..."

Because of my spinal curvature, rear-entry, either when I am on my side or my stomach, also works best for me. I prefer lying on my side with my partner on his side behind me ("spoons" J. calls this position) because it allows me to move as much as I am able although his movements are somewhat restricted. I have wonderful orgasms when he places his top leg over my leg, squeezing the lips of my vulva tightly together which increases the friction on my clitoris. Although I am considerably more confined, I also enjoy intercourse when lying on my stomach if my legs are spread sufficiently to allow deep enough penetration for his balls to rub against my clitoris during the inward thrust.

Like Lola, I, too, take pride in having a tight vagina and using my vaginal muscles to increase the pleasure of both my man and myself. Since it appears that these muscles are not usually affected by polio, cerebral palsy, etc., it is probably possible for many of us to benefit from doing exercises to keep these muscles in the best possible condition.

The pelvic-floor exercises, better known as Kegel exercises (named for Arnold Kegel, a California medical pioneer), originally developed to increase bladder control, have also been found useful for toning and strengthening vaginal muscles, both for better orgasms and to prepare for childbirth (Boston Women's Health Book Collective, 1976). To locate the muscles we are proposing to tone, try to stop urinating once you have begun. Start and stop a few times until you get a feel for where these muscles are and how to contract them. The authors recommend contracting these muscles hard for one second (presumably not while urinating) and then relaxing them. Ten of these contractions and releases make up one set of exercises. Increase the number of sets each day until you work up to twenty in about a month. They can be done while sitting, standing or lying down, while talking on the phone, waiting for an appointment, or listening to a lecture.

Our orgasms, after having been ignored for centuries, have in recent years become a hot topic. Which are best—clitoral or vaginal, how should they be brought about, how many are sufficient and so on. In a sense, men have taken over this intimate domain of ours by their very insistence that we **must** *"come"* each time we have intercourse. Although it is very nice to have orgasms (the more the better) such intense preoccupation with them places unnecessary pressure on both partners and renders an orgasm, which must be spontaneous, far less likely occur.

Only seven of my respondents never had an orgasm during sexual activity. Patricia Maher did not *"know what an orgasm feels like, unless it's in a dream. This is very real."* Mae Evans said, *"I no longer experience orgasm. I am in constant pain. My paraplegic legs are in the way. We still make love, but it's not spontaneous like it used to be. We are still adjusting to the new situation, and it is very hard for both of us."* Marlene C. felt that *"intercourse is very pleasurable and satisfying even though I don't have orgasms, because of the physical closeness and contact with a man I care about."*

Twenty-one women experienced orgasms occasionally during sexual activity; twenty-two experienced them frequently; and eight fortunate women always had orgasms whenever they engaged in sexual activity.

To assume that because a woman does not have sensation in her genital organs, she cannot experience orgasms is a myth. Shere Hite in **The Hite Report** (1977) defined an emotional orgasm as *"a feeling of love and communication with another human beng that reaches a peak, a great welling up of intensity of feeling...wanting to merge and become one person."* The following three women, all paraplegics, describe their experience of emotional orgasm.

Elizabeth Mark stated, *"Sex is, to a great deal emotional. Because I cannot 'feel' sex physically does not mean I do not 'feel' it mentally! I can 'feel' because I want to. I become involved with the 'thought' of what is happening. This makes me feel sexual, warm, open, and excited. I want to be totally smothered by my husband. I want us to come together as one. The orgasm is the fulfillment of togetherness—the two becoming one. The happiness of a warm experience! Amen."*

Helen Beach agreed, *"I don't have any sensations at all below my level of injury which is just below my breast, but, for me, now that I'm in a relationship with a person that I really care about, it's a different experience. It's like ninety per cent of orgasm for me is between my ears because of how I'm feeling about the person that I'm with is what I get excited about...loving the person and being loved.*

"I also get a deep pleasure sensation, whether that's with manual stimulation or penis in vagina or sometimes even with oral sex 'cause I, every once in a while,...can sorta' feel my clitoris, and it isn't what I call 'normal' sensation or it isn't, I think, the same way as prior to my injury but, nonetheless, it's very pleasurable for me, and the deep pleasure sensation with intercourse, and sometimes with manual stimulation too,

sometimes has been able to be orgasmic for me. Where I do have sensation, I'm hypersensitive which developed over the periods of time after my injury where I'm most sensitive around my nipples and the sides of my neck, the back of my neck, on the inside of my arm, on the other side of the elbows, in between my fingers. I just discovered so many places that are very sensuous and some places, when I'm really excited and really turned on, will bring me to the point that feels like a peak of sexual exictement for me....Sometimes, I don't feel a sense of orgasm—and that's O.K.—I still enjoy what's going on....Other times, I'll achieve a whole bunch of orgasms, kind of in a row, like I used to before I broke my back, and that feels good too. Sometimes I'll reach one orgasm that's real intense; at times, I'll reach just one orgasm that's not very intense, but it's still pleasurable in a sense of sexual, a release of sexual tension for me."

Marie R. outlined her experience of orgasm after her injury: *"First, I will explain my level of paralysis. It follows my pelvic bone—higher in the back, down at the hip bone, lower down to the front pelvic area and back up at the other hip bone. I have no feelings, only sensation in the genital area. I have to be very excited sexually to have an orgasm....It usually requires a lot of foreplay and encouragement from my husband so that it requires as much from my mind as it does from my body. I have strong hip kickers and back muscles...and use them for the rhythm movements during intercourse. As the feelings intensify, my whole body strains toward the climax. I feel small shudders or spasms inside which is, I guess, the uterus or cervix, and a feeling of relief and release rushes over my body."*

When asked during which type of sexual activity they are most likely to have orgasms, thirty-six cited heterosexual contact other than intercourse (usually clitoral stimulation although one woman specified anal penetration). Using a scale of 1-10 to measure the intensity of their orgasms, twenty-seven rated them above a five, and, of these, eleven usually had two or more orgasms each time they engaged in sexual activity.

Twenty-seven women listed intercourse as their best source of orgasms. Of these, seventeen estimated their orgasms above a five, but only six regularly experienced a sequence of two or more each time they had intercourse. These are slightly lower ratios, proportionally, than those preferring a partner's direct stimulation other than intercourse.

The most reliable source of orgasms cited by twenty-three women was self-stimulation. Using the same scale, over half of these (13) scored their orgasms higher than five, but they were much less likely to have multiple orgasms (only three).

Masturbation by mechanical means such as vibrators were the preferred means of achieving orgasms for eleven women. Seven of these, a high ratio in comparison with the other groups, evaluated their orgasms above five in intensity. Only, three, however, had more than two orgasms in a row.

Seven women masturbated with inanimate objects (bananas, brush handles, etc.) to achieve orgasms regularly. All rated their orgasms at six or above, but only one woman had more than two sequential orgasms.

One woman cited sexual activity with another woman as the situation in which she was most likely to have orgasms; she said that these were definitely "*tens.*"

Women studied by Shere Hite (1977, pp. 185-7) felt that clitoral orgasms were stronger and more intense than vaginal orgasms which were softer and more diffused over the entire body. 'My respondents apparently concurred, for their most intense orgasms occurred through clitoral stimulation either by a partner or by themselves. Having several orgasms in a row seemed more likely to happen from clitoral stimulation by a partner, however. This contrasts with Hite's findings that more and better orgasms occurred through self-stimulation of the clitoris (1977, pp. 327-8). Twenty-three women were usually orgasmic both ways.

Even though forty-one achieved orgasms easier through some form of masturbation, my respondents overwhelmingly preferred to have them with a partner (61), whether through manual stimulation or intercourse. To me, this is further proof of the greater desire for physical closeness and touching felt by Differently Abled women because of early and/or current deprivation of touching.

Leo Buscaglia, in his splendid little book called *Love* (1972), said that alienation is becoming almost the norm as people continue to retreat further from each other and themselves. To those of us already set apart in some ways, this unfortunate trend may be especially detrimental. In view of this tendency toward isolation, I am particularly excited about the findings in this chapter. Even though I suspected it right along, to know definitively that we are exercising our sexuality in healthy, satisfying ways is very gratifying.

First, we are continuing to reach out to form sexual relationships at a time when so many others are retreating, scared. Most of us are electing to have our orgasms with another person despite the fact that they may be more intense alone. Second, with the understanding and acceptance of our partners, we are striving to devise solutions to any problems we may have in becoming successful sexual partners. Most important, by recognizing on a gut level that we are or can be good lovers able to keep our mates satisfied and happy, we may be able to regain some of the self-worth of which we have been robbed by society's assumptions about us.

With this affirmation comes responsibility, however, and we will discuss a major aspect of this responsibility in the following chapter on birth control.

10

Choices
(Birth Control)

Although there have been a number of articles in various medical and nursing journals discussing whether or not Differently Abled women are able to have babies, there has been virtually nothing about birth control. Our fertility and its regulation is one more facet of our sexuality usually ignored by the professionals who are supposed to be rehabilitating us. The experience of Hot Wheels, spinal cord injured at the age of twenty-two, is typical: *"Nothing was said at the rehab center—a big let-down."* Only seven had received any kind of specialized information as part of their rehabilitation process.

This unfortunate omission has many implications in terms of both our physical health and psychological well-being. Elizabeth Mark, mother of two, echoed the dilemma of many when she said, *"My most basic concern at this point is contraception—I am on birth control pills but realize I cannot take them too many years. No other type of contraception can be used because of infection, etc."*

Seventy-two women did possess general birth control information; the most common sources of it (50 each) were either their doctor or books, magazine articles, or pamphlets. Friends were considered the next best sources (28); followed by parents (15); family planning centers (14); lovers (11); advertisements for contraceptives (11); siblings (10); and teachers (6). Other resources found useful by respondents were T.V. programs (3); counselor (1); school classes (1); men's magazines (1); church meeting (1); and personal research (1). Obviously, a large number of women had obtained their contraception information from more than one source.

When asked whether the data received was correct, fifty-nine women said it was while ten more said that it was only partially so. None had discovered any gross inaccuracies in the information they had received.

Forty-six women said that the birth control pill had been suggested to them, thirty-five of whom had not been advised of the increased risks to their physical health because of reduced mobility (higher possibilities of blood clots). Poodle Gal, who uses a wheelchair, related her experience: "*The doctor was a G.P. and didn't even give me a pelvic exam. He just said that* [women] *sometimes get nauseated, bloated and gain weight and sometimes have headaches. I was to be married in two weeks and was just finishing my period so two days later, I started using my birth control pills....The pills were agreeing with me until four days after we were married. Then, I woke up during the night with a terrible pain in the groin of my left leg. My husband took me to the same doctor the next day, and all he said was that I must have caught the flu and it landed in my groin, as it was inflamed and swollen.*" Later in the day when the pain got worse she "*called the same doctor, and he said, 'Call another doctor—one who knows your disability as you have thrombophlebitis and may need surgery!' Now fourteen-and-a-half years later—my leg still swells, and I have a pain in my groin.*" Lola who had polio, was on the Pill for four months with no problems "*until I got a blood clot under my right knee—thrombophlebitis. I was lucky; it stayed put and dissolved in about a week. IUD was then suggested. I bled when they put it in and had severe cramps until I rejected it by the next morning.*"

Brillig "*was on the Pill for six or seven years through Planned Parenthood. My doctor at the time expressed doubts (not re disability).*" She felt, "*Planned Parenthood not honest about Pill generally.*"

Liz Williams said "*I've consulted a G.P. and two gynecologists....One of the gynecologists was insistent that the pill was the only way (I would be too 'clumsy' using anything else, yet he was also pushing that I should have no trouble using tampons!) and quickly insisted (even after I told him that presently in my life I didn't have the need for a contraceptive) that I take a one-month sample he had and proceeded to write me a prescription that could be refilled twice! It's so hard to know who to believe and who to trust! Fortunately, these three doctors I consulted had good attitudes about discussing these things with me. I just wish they knew specifically about disabled women."*

Laura, who contracted polio when she was three-and-a-half years old, agreed, saying she *"learned of side effects from disabled women who had trouble with them."* There is a need for someone to conduct scientific studies on the safety of the contraceptive pill in relation to the various types of disabling conditions; the results should be widely disseminated, for only by having the real facts can we make educated decisions about our bodies.

Twenty-four women **were** told of the possible negative side effects if they used the pill. A rehabilitation doctor advised Pooh Grayson *"against continued use of the pill because it might increase the possibility of blood clots. The alternative suggested was to have my tubes tied."* For Poodle Gal, *"The only other alternative suggested to the pill was a hysterectomy, but it was dropped as surgery was too great a risk to my health."* (The solution in this instance was a vasectomy for her husband.) The advice given to Helen Beach was *"that I run a higher risk of a clot stopping in my lungs than an able-bodied woman; however, my muscle spasticity helps reduce this."*

Seventeen women received no recommendations other than the pill. The diaphragm was suggested to ten women. Besides Lola, the IUD was seen as a viable alternative for eight women. Foam was also recommended to eight. Condoms or tubal ligations were each mentioned six times.

Despite all of the above discussion, the birth control pill was still the most popular form of contraception and used by fifteen women. Orthonovum was the brand most frequently mentioned (5), followed by Oracon (2), Norlestrin (1), and Norinyl 1.50 (1).

A rather permanent solution, sterilization of one of the partners, was elected by eleven women. Four male partners had vasectomies while seven women had either tubal ligations or hysterectomies.

I was concerned that some may have been pressured into sterilization, as the mentally impaired often are, but, happily, this does not appear to be true. Martha Merriweather's *"decision to have a tubal ligation was totally mine, and I was under no pressure from anyone. My husband agreed with me, and we sought to have that done together. The decision was made because I found that when I was pregnant with my second child, the care of the first became more difficult, physically speaking, and I did not feel* that I had the stamina to raise more than two children." "At age eighteen," Anet "delivered a stillborn baby. My mother then suggested the pill, but it was not yet widely available. I started taking Enovid after my second child (live) but at one point could not afford them so I got pregnant....Tubal ligation fought for and won over incredible obstacles."

Five women used diaphragms. Michelle used "**Ortho diaphragm. I'm left-handed, had to learn to use right hand. Have to have something solid to lean on to get it in. Much patience, sometimes many trials.**"

Two women used intrauterine devices (IUD's), one of whom specified the copper T. For other respondents, this method has been something less than successful. Besides the experiences of Lola and Dahtee, Ebony said, "*I went for the first check-up, and it was halfway out...And I also bled too heavy.*"

Three women used the rhythm method, foam, abstinence, or their partners wore condoms. April named "**Conceptrol because it comes in throwaway plastic applicators, thus freeing my partner from the added burden of washing the applicator.**" Woodie used "**a spermicidal suppository...simple to use which is inserted ten minutes before intercourse...I do think that all sexually active women should have some form of birth control.**" Because none of these contraceptives is very effective alone, it is necessary to use a combination of two for reliability.

When asked if they ever requested their lovers to assist with birth control, twenty-four replied that they did not. Cindy, whose polio occurred when she was thirteen, "**never used anything. My partner assumed the responsibility.**" Jessica, an interviewer from Texas, said, "*I have not asked, but if I did, I would expect him to cooperate.*" Liz Williams added, "*There are instances where I would imagine this could add to the experience.*"

Twelve women did request their partner to help with birth control, and the results were mixed. Samantha's "**partner felt comfortable assisting with birth control devices, even if it was a break. We tried to include it in sexual foreplay.**" April admitted "**great embarrassment about having to ask my partner to help with birth control.**" Pamela "*felt fine; he didn't.*"

Somewhat more limited cooperation was recorded by Julia: "*he buys my pills,*" and Helen Beach: "*I ask him to share the responsibility and help me to remember to take my birth control pills and catheterize afterwards.*"

Thirteen women used no birth control, of whom eight were not currently engaged in sexual relationships and two were beyond childbearing age. Since the other three did not state that they were actively trying to become pregnant, it appears that they may not be using birth control because of the physical difficulty of it. If so, this is unfortunate, for there are a number of options.

Of the mechanical-technical contraceptive choices, condoms (worn over the man's penis) are about the easiest to obtain as they are available at drugstores or by mail from ads in the backs of many magazines. Made from very thin latex or even animal skin, with lubrication and in various textures, they are much less obnoxious than previously. Used together with spermicide foam or cream, they are quite effective.

Many have found spermicides convenient to use. Easily purchased in most drugstores, several brands, such as Emko, Conceptrol, and Ortho-Creme, come in pre-filled disposable applicators which minimize the bother of using them. Disadvantages are that they must be inserted high in the vagina within a half-hour of intercourse, may cause skin irritations for either the woman or her partner, and have a bad taste if engaging in oral sex. Their advantages are that they are readily available without a prescription, are easy to insert, and are considered least harmful of the contraceptives.

Newest on the market, according to the authors of **Contraceptive Technology, 1980-1981** (Hatcher et al., 1980, pp. 95-98) are spermicide suppositiories. They recommend Encare as being the most effective (99% sure if used **every** time one has intercourse) because it foams upon contact with the heat of your body, thereby providing a dense barrier to the cervix, and, since it is pre-measured in the correct dosage, there is no problem with insufficient pressure in the applicator or not enough spermicide being inserted. To allow time for melting, it must be inserted high in the vagina at least ten minutes before intercourse, but since it will be effective for one hour it could probably be inserted just before lovemaking begins, unless you're into marathon foreplay. Again, skin irritation may occur in either partner. Because other brands of spermicide suppositiories do not possess the foaming characteristic, they are not as reliable.

Because they are only effective for short periods of time, all spermicides should be used every time one has intercourse, and all directions in the packages should be read and followed carefully. Advertising for some of these products is often vague so be sure that you have, in fact, purchased a contraceptive and not merely a vaginal deodorant. Also, since spermicides leak out when you are once again in an upright position, you may wish to wear a tampon or a mini-pad for a short period of time afterward.

Spermicides are said to be the safest form of contraception a woman can use, but Rosenblum (1976, p. 28) conjectures that their use might be at least partially responsible for the rising incidence of birth defects. Although no study was cited to substantiate this, he reminds us that spermicides are, in fact, poison intended to kill sperm and questions the type of damage that may occur to the sperm which sometimes do survive to fertilize an egg.

A diaphragm is a bowl-like device, usually made of latex, which, when filled with spermicidal cream or jelly, is placed inside the vagina up against the cervix, thus providing a double barrier against sperm attempting to enter the cervix. For a snug fit, they come in a wide range of millimeter sizes and have one of three types of spring (flat spring, coil spring and arcing spring) in the rim. Although the rim is round, it can be squeezed flat for insertion either by hand or by hooking it across a plastic wand type of instrument called an introducer. For someone with limited manual dexterity, the introducer makes the correct insertion and removal of the diaphragm much easier. The diaphragm can be inserted up to six hours before intercourse and must be left in place for at leat six hours afterwards.

Both diaphragm and introducer must be prescribed either by a doctor or family planning agency clinician because correct fit and proper placement are essential for this to be an effective means of contraception. One is usually given instructions and then expected to practice placing and removing it several times under supervision to gain confidence about using the correct procedure.

Disadvantages of the diaphragm are that it may cause cramps, bladder pressure or irritation, or cystitis when left in place the recommended amount of time. Also, occasionally, one is allergic to the latex or rubber from which it is constructed, or one's anatomy may not allow a tight enough fit. Studies differ on the diaphragm's reliability in preventing pregnancy. Inconsistent use due to some women's aversion to the necessary self-manipulation may be a factor in the discrepancy (Hatcher et al., pp. 76-78). Even though I feel that I could learn to use it properly by means of the introducer, I dislike this aspect enough not to consider it a suitable contraceptive for myself.

Seventeen women felt that abortion was also a valid method of birth control; fifty women did not. Jay Kirfirst felt abortions "**should not be even mentioned in light of all birth control methods available—though often wished I were not born.**"

When asked if they thought a woman should have an abortion if the child is known to have been damaged and will be born with a handicapping condition, twenty-four respondents said that she should have the abortion. Some of the reactions were strong. Daisy D. exclaimed, "*My God—don't do it to a person—abortion is* **better** *than suffering a handicap.*" Samantha added, "*When you get right down to it, there is a lot of pain in being handicapped.*" Colette, whose Fredrich's ataxia began when she was five years old, felt "*if that is the case, then there is no question about it. I know that I led a drastically lonely life because I was shunned by 'would-be' friends and over-protective parents. I don't believe any child should have to go through with this....*" E. B. Browning responded, "*I would not bring a severely disabled child into the world (and how could I tell?)*" Sally Smith concurred, "*...even though my religion teaches against it, I believe it would be the thing to do.*"

The following backed their opinions with sound, well-considered reasoning. Linda, a mother of a five-year-old son, felt "*very strongly that a woman should decide whether she wants an abortion or not. A mother's attitude concerning a handicapped child would have a great effect on that child's adjustment.*" Larkin pointed out, "*In cases where it is genetically passed on, no one but the handicapped parent would know better if it was worth making a new person to live with it.*" Connie L. felt "*the child has a right to live, is not less than others, and yet it seems merciful to end life before it really begins in earnest, though I imagine the fetus struggles against being killed just as we do. It's probably best to have an abortion unless the parents are determined to do everything in their power to give the child as full and independent a life as possible.*" Jenny Jones, a twenty-eight-year-old claims representative, said, "*I think it would have its place for those handicaps which are so severe that a child would be a vegetable and beyond any hope. However, in most cases, a great deal of talent might be lost since the disabled person can accomplish a great deal if given the proper assistance and encouragement.*"

Summer wisely observed that "*aborting all children who will be disabled is like trying to make a perfect race. I feel abortion should be made available to all women for all pregnancies, but I do not feel that women should be pushed toward abortion if it is found a child will be handicapped. I think the good and bad points of a disability should be made clear, and the doctor or counselor should remain neutral.*"

Ten women objected intensely to abortions when the child would be born Differently Abled.

Lola argued, "*If abortions are immoral, I cannot conceive of them being more moral if the child has less of a right to be born, or to live, or is less of a human being, than any other child. If abortion is murder, as the anti-abortionists claim, why would aborting a handicapped child be less than murder? Is she/he less human? Does she/he have fewer rights? And, if some people think this is so (and they obviously do) what about the handicapped children and adults who are too old to be 'aborted'? I find this kind of thinking quite threatening. If someone should decide I shouldn't be allowed to live before I'm born, perhaps they might also decide I don't have a right to live after I'm born.*"

Simone, a bi-lateral amputee from birth, felt it was not her "*choice to decide who lives or who dies, or I might not be here now.*" A Canadian social worker/editor, Nora Ellen concurred but in a slightly lighter tone, "*Against them—the implication is that I would have been aborted if it had been shown that I would be handicapped, and I am enjoying a hell of a good life.*" Yvonne Winters, an Ohio teacher, declared, "*I really think abortions are unnecessary even if the child would be handicapped. I feel that this would be the destruction of human life, and we do not have this right.*" Deena, whose religion does not believe in abortions, said, "*If I do have a disabled child, I would bring it up just as my parents brought me up but with some changes since doctors know better now about different techniques.*"

A few women objected with some qualifiers. Melanie Marie said, "*Unless the child would be severely retarded, I would not abort. I believe a fetus is an alive human being from conception.*" Yana Da Shana felt that she would consider abortion "*only if the child would be so abnormal that he would spend his life shut away in an institution, and even then I would be reluctant to recommend such a step.*"

Sixty-two women had never had an abortion, but ten women had. Bernice, a New Jersey mother of two daughters, said her abortion "*was the greatest shock of my life.*" Lola discussed the reasons for her recent abortion: "*My main reason for having the abortion was that I'm not married, and I would have needed help taking care of the baby....I'm very doubtful if I could have got the help—since I can't even get the help I need (an attendant). If my mother suddenly couldn't help me (which is quite possible—she's quite old), I'd have to go to a nursing home. Can you see me taking care of a baby in a nursing home? That would be funny if it wasn't so sad.*

"*Is abortion right or wrong?*" she pondered, "*Before I had* [it] *I was fairly pro-abortion in an off-hand sort of way. Becoming pregnant and having the abortion forced me to look into my feelings about it—very deeply. I'm not so sure anymore. I tend to feel it's wrong unless it's really a life and death matter."*

Fertility awareness is the safest form of birth control because it does not involve surgery or the introduction of any foreign or chemical substances into the body but consists of understanding and utilizing the natural signs given by your body to indicate ovulation is occurring. Largely due to the unreliability of the rhythm method (30% effectiveness rate according to Rosenblum) natural contraception has been in disfavor. Recently, however, the unpleasant and even dangerous side effects of the Pill and the IUD, as well as the newer, more dependable methods of detecting ovulation, have refocused attention on the utilization of natural physiological patterns. To maximize effectiveness, some combination of two of the natural methods of birth control is recommended by both Rosenblum and Hatcher et al.

Perhaps the oldest and best known of these is the calendar method. According to **Contraceptive Technology 1980-1981**, it is first essential to record the length of your menstrual cycle for at least eight months. The first day of menstrual bleeding is considered Day One. After you have recorded this information for the last eight months, you can compute your probable fertile period by subtracting eighteen days from the length of your shortest cycle, which is the first day of your fertile period and subtracting eleven days from the length of your longest cycle, which is the last day of it. For example, if your shortest cycle is twenty-five days, the seventh day following the onset of your menstrual period will be the first day of your fertile period, and if your longest cycle is thirty days, the last day of your fertile time will be the nineteenth day of your cycle. Therefore, you have a thirteen-day span during which the likelihood of becoming pregnant is quite great if you engage in sexual intercourse.

If the calendar method is the only birth control you intend to use, the computations should be backed up by either of the basal body temperature or the mucus methods, according to the authors of **Contraceptive Technology**.

The basal body temperature method (BBT) consists of recording your lowest body temperature daily (usually immediately after waking up each morning) for at least a three-month period. It is important to use a basal body thermometer rather than an oral or rectal one. Usually one's body temperature rises 0.4°-0.8° immediately after ovulation has occurred. The authors say that although some women have a noticeable drop in temperature just before the rise, it should not be counted upon. The temperature will probably remain higher until the beginning of the next menstrual cycle; however, since the life-span of the egg is only about twenty-four hours and sperm are only capable of fertilizing it for about two days, the length of the actual fertile period is three days. Because one's body temperature can be elevated from other causes, such as infection, too warm bedclothes, etc., the BBT method by itself can be quite unreliable, but, used in combination with one of the other methods, it can be useful for pinpointing the fertile time more accurately.

The third method is the mucus method developed by Drs. John and Lynn Billings upon request by the Roman Catholic Church (1976, p. 52). Again, you must keep track of your menstrual cycle for several months but what is recorded this time is the amount and consistency of the mucus in your vagina. Hatcher and his co-authors (1980, pp. 108-111) advise checking your vagina by inserting a finger each time you go to the bathroom during this base period. Right after the menstrual period, one's vagina is usually moist but not wet. As ovulation approaches, the amount of mucus will increase and become thin, white and slippery—like egg white. It can be stretched three inches or more between the fingers. The peak of this slippery transparent mucus should be the time of ovulation, and one is fertile for three days after that. Since Rosenblum postulates that as ovulation approaches the function of this mucus may be to keep the sperm alive until ovulation can occur, it would be wise to refrain from intercourse for about three days prior to the peak of this slippery mucus. The cervix, at this time, also becomes softer, more pliable, and its opening (the os) dilates slightly, thus, also facilitating the entrance of the sperm.

There are a few drawbacks in using this method. Because the presence of semen or spermicides in the vagina will make an accurate assessment of the mucus virtually impossible, it is essential to abstain from intercourse around the expected time of ovulation. Also, one cannot douche because the mucus will be washed away. Differently Abled women with limited hand and finger dexterity may have some difficulty utilizing this method, but a husband, lover, or willing attendant could help.

The Natural Birth Control Book by Art Rosenblum has easy to read instructions for the procedures outlined above as well as some more experimental contraceptive theories I will discuss later. It is $4.95 at local bookstores or from the Aquarian Research Foundation, Box P-4120, 5620 Morton St., Philadelphia, PA 19144. Also

130

available for $7.50 is a kit containing the book, a calendar, a basal body thermometer, and charts to facilitate record-keeping. Compact kits which also contain a mucus spoon (for women reluctant or unable to insert fingers in their vaginas) are available from Telesis Corporation, P.O. Box 681, San Fransisco, CA 94101 (Hatcher et al., p. 114). Such supplies are frequently available at family planning centers or drugstores.

Two newer methods of natural birth control, although they have not, at present, been subjected to sufficiently rigorous study to ensure effectiveness, may be promising for Differently Abled women because they do not require any manual dexterity.

One is the Jonas-Rechnitz or Astrological Birth Control Method (1976, pp. 24-29), first discovered in the Iron Curtain countries of Hungary and Czechslovakia. This system, based on the premise that as well as the time of ovulation we have already been discussing, every woman has each month an additional fertile time related to the positions of the sun and the moon at her birth. Used in conjunction with another natural method, studies have shown an effectiveness rate of slightly more than 97%, according to Rosenblum, who predicts that if it had been used exclusively with the mucus or ovulation method, the effectiveness rate would have been proved to be at least 98%.

To use this method, it is necessary to know as accurately as possible your time and place of birth, for a woman is said to be the most fertile for the twenty-four hours immediately preceding the angle of the moon when it is in the same relation to the sun as it was when she was born. Allowing for a two-and-a-half-day life span for sperm, it is necessary to abstain from intercourse or use a spermicide and/or diaphragm for this length of time prior to this fertile period as well as twelve hours following it to allow a safety margin for any possible miscalculations—a total of about four days. This fertile period occurs about thirteen times a year. When it coincides with the period of ovulation, fertility is considerably increased. Because birth control pills have been shown to upset both the ovulation and cosmic body rhythms, if they have been used recently, one must wait at least three months or until menstrual cycles have become fairly regular before relying on these calculations.

For easy calculation, **The Natural Birth Control Book** contains computerized charts of the sun-moon angles from January, 1931 through December, 1981, and sets for the years 1982-2,000 can be obtained from the Aquarian Research Foundation for $3 per set. Included are easy instructions for doing the computations, as well as the variations if you're not sure of the exact time and place of your birth. It is said that forced birth, such as Caesarian section, does not influence the cosmic cycles.

The other method, involving mind control over conception (Ibid., pp. 12-23), should be considered theoretical at this time. Again, in combination with other natural methods such as the ovulation (mucus) and cosmic fertility cycles, it consists of thinking one's self not pregnant should intercourse occur during these designated fertile periods. Women describe it variously as visualizing a barrier of light around the egg which cannot be penetrated by sperm, thinking positively about the onset of one's menstrual period, feeling that one is protected from pregnancy by God, and so on.

It sounds like mumbo-jumbo except that this system, first described over fifty years ago by Bronislaw Malinowski in a book about the Trobriand Islanders called **The Sexual Life of Savages** has been confirmed by more recent anthropological field studies. The women who have utilized this sytem of psychic birth control with any success have been women trained in meditation or other types of non-Western philosophies of mind over matter. Since both men and women are now being trained to control their internal organs in ways that were never previously thought possible, I tend to agree with Rosemblum that this "**conscious control of conception could easily become the norm in the not-too-distant future.**"

The preceding summaries are meant to be merely an overview of what is currently available and a look at future trends. Details in the books cited should be read fully before deciding on any particular method. Also, it is advisable, and even necessary when considering the use of some forms, to consult your doctor or family planning agency such as Planned Parenthood. At the latter, some services are free, and contraceptive supplies are dispensed at nominal cost.

Largely as a result of the mistaken assumption that we are in no need of such services, there may be a problem (as there is in Ann Arbor) with the family planning clinic you seek being architecturally inaccessible. If this is the case, the administrators should be politely reminded that if they receive any federal money for their program, under Sec. 504 of the Rehabilitation Act they are required to provide you with services. You could refer them both to the Regulations themselves and to a great little booklet called **Within Reach: Providing Family Planning Services to Physically Disabled Women**, which is available from the Task Force on Concerns of Physically Disabled Women, Planned Parenthood-Snohomish County, 2730 Hoyt, Everett, Washington 98201.

The choice of whether or not to bring a new life into the world is our responsibility just as much as it is any woman's. We must not allow others to rob us of this choice which is, in effect, what happens when we are unable to avail ourselves of the same contraceptive services available to other women.

11

Labor of Love
(Childbirth and Child-Rearing)

Motherhood is an important facet of female sexuality both as a frequent end result of the sex act and as a cultural and emotional expression of womanliness. As reported earlier in this book, when respondents were asked which activities made them feel most womanly, eight echoed Pooh Grayson's list of priorities: *"Sex, having a baby, being a wife and mother...."* As external proof of the ability to participate in sexual intercourse, motherhood also appeared to be significant to some mates as well. Linda said of her husband, *"he wouldn't have married me if I couldn't have children or were more disabled."*

There was no shortage of children among my respondents. Twenty-four women had a total of forty-six children. Thirty-three of these children were born to seventeen women after they had become Differently Abled. Eight said that their specific physical condition caused them no particular problems during pregnancy. Colleen Moore said that she went into labor early but was not sure that the factors were related. (They may have been, for premature labor is a possibility for women with spinal cord injuries, according to Kolodny, et al. in the **Textbook of Human Sexuality for Nurses,** 1979, p. 254).

Nine said that being Differently Abled did complicate their pregnancy. Three mentioned just general discomfort associated with the increased size and weight which made daily living activities more difficult. Hot Wheels said she *"felt like an elephant."* More frequent urination and less bladder control were also mentioned. This is a common problem for able-bodied women which may be accentuated for the Differently Abled. Pamela, a polio quad, found that during pregnancy her breathing ability was decreased and she had to sleep in an iron lung. Linda disclosed, *"I had trouble getting pregnant because medication I was taking (probably Mandelamine) was keeping my pH at a level which was killing the sperm. This was overcome by changing the time of day I took my medication and douching with soda prior to intercourse to keep my chemical balance long enough for the sperm to reach the ovum."* She continued, *"My family doctor didn't think I would have trouble with childbirth. I went into autonomic hyperreflexia and could have had a stroke. Some doctors think a spinal block would have prevented this."*

Women who had already become Differently Abled at the time they were considering raising a family were asked what medical advice they had received about pregnancy. Thirteen women had been given recommendations against it as often because of the difficulty of child-rearing as because of the contraindications of their specific physical condition. Nine women were encouraged to have children by their physicians. As always, opinions were mixed. Elizabeth Mark, who has two children, quoted, *"My O.B. said 'fine'; my plastic surgeon said 'You're stupid'—my last O.B. said I should limit to two children saying 'I am high risk'. I know what I can do. I love my children and plan more. If I listened to each doctor's opinion I have known, I would not be where I am now! I know what's best for me."*

As with marriage and other visible proofs of our sexuality, we are bound to be given opinions, wanted or not, by family and community members. Martha Merriweather recalled, *"I became pregnant three months after being discharged from the hospital, and that really upset my family. They wanted to know what I was going to do with the baby, why I was having a baby. I was accused of being totally out of my mind for having a baby, but my babies are eighteen and fourteen now* [at the time of response] *and I feel that I have done as good a job as any able-bodied parent in raising them."* Returning to the subject of the first pregnancy, she continued, *"I even had one woman come up to me when I was very obviously eight-nine months pregnant and say, 'You can't be pregnant.' I found that rather humorous."* Brillig observed, *"Hospitals made a point of segregating me from other mothers. One even tried to segregate me from a friend who had a baby at the same time—who put up a real battle to room with me."*

In an article entitled "Can A Wheelchair-Bound Woman Have a Baby?" in the Spring, 1981, issue of **Accent on Living** (p. 78), Jean Moore advises a trip to the maternity ward well ahead of the anticipated delivery date. One should inspect the set-up of the rooms to be used and discuss with the staff any observations you may have about possible problems. Make a list of your needs for both yourself and the nursing staff so that, in the excitement of labor, nothing is forgotten.

A number of mothers were kind enough to share with us how they worked out the logistics of Differently Abled motherhood. Brillig continued, *"Used crib that opened up instead of down. Nursed last three for convenience. Kept babies in basket by bed so could feed and diaper in bed...*[toddlers were] *tied to front door."* Hot Wheels *"used a bridge table as a changing table."* Shirley O'Hara, mother of two, remembered, *"having the necessary baby things at counter height, crib mattress raised....Also, had a bottle warmer on the night stand to heat formula for night feeding. I had the crib or bassinet next to the bed. I bathed the baby in the kitchen sink lined with a towel."* Linda *"used bathette to bathe him when he was an infant. When he got too big for that, my husband had to bathe him in the tub until recently. He is now old enough (four years)...to turn the water off and on with supervision and cooperates with me by coming close enough to let me bathe him and wash his hair."*

Marie R., whose first pregnancy turned out to be twin boys, had lots of good advice: *"To bathe them, I had a small portable baby's bath tub which I slipped into a large cloth bag (like a pillowcase) that I made to fit the tub. This made a sling inside the tub for the baby to lie in. Then I had two hands free to bathe them and to keep my balance also. I used this method till they could sit well themselves.*

"When the twins were babies (under twelve months)," she continued, *"they each learned to balance themseles while lying on my lap while I was pushing myself and could not hold onto them. It was like instinct for them to balance when they knew I had to let go of them....To pick them up from the floor...till they could walk, I would bend over, extend one of my arms out, roll them over that arm, push myself up with the other arm, and hoist them up onto my lap. I usually used my right arm for lifting*

them because it's the strongest arm....

"*I can't remember taking the twins out in the car by myself until they were about nine or ten months old...the car seats were about six to eight inches from the side door, and I would get the wheelchair as close as possible while one of the boys was on my lap. I picked up the baby at the waist and leaned into the car. I would lose my balance because of the baby's weight, and as I leaned in that direction I extended my arms toward the car-seat and plop—there he would be, and I never missed either.*"

Daisy D. "*hired part-time help. Kept relatives in control. Was loving but firm and consistent. Was his pal. Made sure all helpers respected that I was Momma/Boss.*"

To carry baby on a lap, Jean Moore (1981, p.79) recommends a sturdy tray, "*secured by a bolt and butterfly nut through a hole in one arm of the chair.*" She covered it with a foam pad enclosed in waterproof material and used split diapers to anchor it and the baby to the tray.

Baby's safety and security once she/he became mobile was a concern for some respondents. Shirley O'Hara shared, "*The one thing that used to scare me was when they started toddling that they would run from me and I could not chase them so I usually had a stroller when going out and a fenced-in yard....I started very early with 'no no' if they were in a situation where they might get hurt' and they were quite good.*"

Martha Merriweather said, "*There were some physical adjustments we had to make. My husband built a play-pen with raised legs so I would be able to pick the baby up, and then we just kept chopping the legs off as the baby grew—when he could get to his knees, the legs of the playpen had to be shortened. I found that I had to keep my children in the playpen until they could walk because I could not pick them up from a creeping position. However, contrary to what I have read with regard to keeping children in a play-pen like this, as far as stifling their curiosity, etc., I can say that it had no effect like that on my children. They're very bright....They are successful in school....They were completely happy in the play-pen....I think if there's enough love, if there is enough time spent with the child, if you talk to the child, if you read to the child, it is not going to retard them mentally in any way.*"

As we have seen, children are adaptable. Although not a mother herself, Larkin participated a great deal in the rearing of her friend's daughter and told of this experience:"*Much of C.'s first year was spent on my lap board. I fed her, held her. I used to worry that I could not run and pick her up when she fell or knocked her head, but even by the age of eighteen months she understood. With anyone else, she would scream until they came to her, but when I was babysitting she would run to me, climb onto the lap board, and then start screaming."*

Most mothers stressed the need for good communication, discipline, and mutual respect. Pooh Grayson described, *"With the help of my husband and attendant, I have achieved a physical closeness with my child. When an infant, I fed her and held her on a pillow on my lap board or on my bed. I used a cloth baby carrier tied around me when we went out. When others tended to her needs, I was nearby so she would know I was in charge. It has paid off—now she sits (and rides) on my lap and romps and cuddles with me a lot. I rely on others to follow through on discipline that I cannot carry out myself. Once or twice, I resorted to biting her to let her know I am not as helpless as she may think. I have also chased her in my chair. Most of my discipline is verbal, and most of the time she respects my wishes."* Anet agreed, *"Communication and respect are the key when dealing with any kind of human relationships. It's particularly vital for a disabled mother to spend a great deal of time with her infants. She shouldn't delegate care to another person. If the disabled mother is unable to diaper and bathe the baby, she can at least have the baby with her and talk to the infant. I had to develop a verbal rapport with my children as early as possible. I had to establish trust and respect."*

Samantha said, *"Since my child was two when I was disabled, there were no special problems other than teaching her to keep things out of the way—and to strictly obey and stay close in public (especially when I was in a wheelchair)."*

Vargo (op. cit., p. 110) says that it is important for Differently Abled mothers to concentrate on their *"asset values"* rather than comparisons with other mothers. By doing so, they can gain self-confidence in their maternal abilities, which may have been diminished by society's emphasis on normality, and respect themselves for the unique qualities they possess.

How did my respondents feel about motherhood for the Differently Abled? Seven were clearly positive. Pooh, with her usual enthusiasm, exclaimed, *"Great! Discipline is difficult; there is frustration in not being able to do things for and with a child. The joys far outweigh the frustrations—being part of the growth of a child. The child is exposed to a lot of different experiences with a disabled mother.*" Pamela agreed, "*It's great! It is demanding, exhausting, but very rewarding.*"

Poodle Gal mentioned a different aspect of parenting: "*We have an adopted thirteen-year-old daughter and want other handicapped couples to consider the idea too. We had to wait for six years to get our girl, as being handicapped puts a couple on the bottom of their waiting list! The child that they finally had for us was six years old and handicapped, and we had wanted a two-or three-year-old and healthy! We thank God for her. The only problem that we have had is a 'behavioral' one, since our child was already six years when we became her parents.*"

Marie R. recalled her change of attitudes: "*Before I was married, I didn't think I would want children because of my disability. Not long after marriage, I wanted to give my husband children like any other woman and because that is where our love led to. Depending on the handicap, of course, I don't think handicapped women should be discouraged from becoming wives and mothers.*"

"*Well, it wasn't my first choice of procedures,*" Brillig admitted wryly, "*but, having the disability, I didn't feel like foregoing motherhood. I was confident in my reproductive powers. Arrogant? I grew up feeling motherhood was part of life—disability doesn't change that.*"

A divorced mother of three, Jane Grant touched on an important political issue when she said, "*I feel very strongly that a disabled mother should not have her children taken away from her if she has shown that she can care for them.*"

Although, at the time of their responses, they were not mothers, the following also expressed positive feelings about motherhood. Jessica declared, "*If a woman wants to be a mother, she should be, regardless of a disability, and if she feels she can handle it.*" Mary Jones felt she "*could raise a child as well as another mother.*"

Three women, none of whom were mothers, were ambivalent on the subject of combining motherhood with their specific physical conditions. Liz Williams wondered, "*if I could be the mother I would want to be. As far as teaching my children all they should know, I feel greatly frustrated at my inadequacies, and I don't think this is a helpful aspect for a mother to have,*" and then she added, "*Of course, part of me wants the experience of bearing a child to prove to myself that I can do it.*" Marlene C. said, "*I would love to adopt a child, but I question my ability to raise a child alone.*" Volunteered Julia, "*I never wanted children even before I became disabled. I think it's okay if the mother can allow herself to let another woman, possibly a 'nanny' to help with raising them.*"

In speaking of the counselor's role in helping family members adjust to the mother becoming Differently Abled, Vargo, (op. cit., p. 109) says, "*Young children are often curious about mother's condition and may feel some fear and aversion towards the disability, particularly if it is accompanied by disfigurement.*" Although certainly my respondents' children have displayed what I consider ordinary curiosity about the specific physical conditions of their mothers, I did not detect any fear or aversion in their responses as recorded by their mothers.

When very young, they seemed to accept it as natural. The attitude of Shirley O'Hara's children was "'*Don't all mothers walk like that?' Finally, I guess a school mate asked my son, 'Why does your mother walk funny?' and he simply said, 'She had polio', and that was that. He used to follow me around with a screwdriver to tighten my bolts on my braces, and whenever they found a screw on the floor, they'd ask me if it was mine.*"

Martha Merriweather figured her children's "*biggest problem was other children saying, 'What's wrong with your mother?' and as far as they were concerned, there was nothing wrong with their mother, and, in fact, that was the answer I heard them give a couple of times, which rather amused me. When my son was about four, one day he came home from the neighbors, and he had big tears in his eyes. I asked him what was wrong, and he said, 'Well, Mary doesn't have a wheelchair to do her housework in. She has to stand up to do it all.' He really felt a great deal of sympathy for her situation.*"

"*My disability is no mystery to my children,*" Anet declared. "*We've always talked about it, and I think their questions were answered before they were asked. I encouraged them to see me and know about me (and other kinds of disabilities as well).*"

A few children had mixed feelings. Joan C., a bi-lateral amputee since the age of twenty-five, said, "*My children (teenagers) have accepted my disability completely—they forget I'm disabled until I am at a function where all others are able-bodied—then they seem embarrassed....I am learning to hear their feelings and not defend myself or attempt to rationalize.*" Samantha said, "*At first, she accepted it as natural and wanted crutches when she grew up. Then she 'wished' I didn't have to have them—then she wanted more specifics as to why I did and when I wouldn't need them.*"

The average age that children began asking questions about their mothers' specific physical conditions was 4.5 years for boys and 5.4 years for girls. I'm not even going to speculate on the reasons that the boys seemed more curious than the girls, but will leave that for the child psychologists among us. The questions were typical of those we've already seen, dealing mostly with mobility (13), followed by questions about when they would improve (9). I recall a friend's three-year-old daughter reassuring me when I couldn't zip up her snowsuit that I'd be able to do it "*when I grew up*". Linda mused, "*My son is four years old and just asks why I am in a wheelchair and why can't I walk. I tell him I was hit by a truck and hurt very bad. He is still quite young for it to affect him. I am still concerned how it will affect him later—will other children tease him and how will he handle it?*"

Nineteen women answered the questions honestly and directly in terms the children could understand. Two preferred to use medical terms to explain their situations.

In summing up, it appeared that most of the children had healthy attitudes toward their mothers being Differently Abled. Every family is unique in some way, and every child must accept and adjust to her/his particular situation. In a book entitled ***In My Heart I'm Still Dancing*** (Strauss, 1979), Susan Strauss says of her mother, whose polio occurred when Susan was three years old, "*There were differences and constraints and responsibilities when I was growing up that were imposed by the situation of Mother's being handicapped, but in the end it was who she was, not how, that counted.*" (p. 136). This is a beautiful tribute which I expect could be echoed by most. if not all, of the children of my respondents.

The mothers, too, were justifiably proud of their childrearing accomplishments. Hot Wheels said, "*I have managed very well—I was divorced when my son was nineteen months and have been alone since.*" Shirley O'Hara admitted, "*I was a better mother than most. I improvised and managed everything well. I raised the children almost by myself and also put one through college, and one almost is finished. I may have been overly maternal, but I guess I was always proving to myself and everyone else that I could do it as well or better. The children are the joy of my life.*" Jane Grant felt, "*My children have matured earlier as they have to help me by picking up, keeping their room clean, etc. I talk to them a lot regarding how we live as a family. We have a lot of so-called 'rap-sessions', assurances of my love, etc."*

Several mothers ended with words of advice for those of us contemplating motherhood.

Daisy D. recommended, *"Be armed with love and the best respected, most recent cross-section of knowledge available. Always be boss over others who help you with your child's care. Have a child for the right reasons,"* she emphasized, *"Do not make a child compensate for your disability or to act out your lost dreams. Do inform the child and give a lot to the public so child finds you're O.K. by the public, and he can answer dumb questions they ask him with smooth confidence. Expose child to every positive creative stimuli so he [she] can be confident and flourish on his [her] own when grown. Your bravery will rub off."* Samantha also stressed, *"A child should not be born to prove ability, womanhood, or sexuality."*

Pooh pointed out, *"I feel the child needs to know the extent of the disability and the limitations. He [she] needs to know you love him [her] and you mean what you say—for discipline." "I never thought about the implications of my disability; just wanted to be a mother,"* exclaimed Anet, *"I do think that disabled young people should be knowledgeable about the implications—perhaps more opportunities to care for small children in order to get a feel for what it might be like."*

Marie R. stressed, *"Something a handicapped mother must remember—your children will be very accepting of you and adaptable to you. They are much tougher than you first think, and my three boys have survived living with me very well....I wouldn't change one minute of our life together—I thank God for blessing me with my wonderful husband and three beautiful boys."*

12

The Great Release
(Masturbation)

A necessary step in the development of one's sexuality is to become intimately acquainted with one's own body—what makes it feel good, what makes it feel bad, which parts feel most sensuous when touched, etc. *"Of course, that goes without saying,"* we might respond glibly, and yet, eleven respondents seldom or never masturbated because they did not know the location of their bodies' pleasure points. This is probably not unusual even in this so-called age of sexual enlightenment. Lonnie Garfield Barbach in her very helpful book, *For Yourself: The Fulfillment of Female Sexuality*, recommends studying one's genitals in a mirror and experimenting with various types of touch in different areas to learn what is most pleasurable.

Babies just naturally explore their own bodies as a part of their immediate environment. They aren't masturbating as they play with their fingers, toes, genitals; they are merely exploring what feels good. All too soon, their hands are slapped as they are told *"Naughty!"* and they quickly learn to associate touching themselves, especially if it's pleasurable, with wrongdoing.

Men masturbate more easily than women probably because their most erotic zone, the penis, is so exposed that it can rub on clothing or other external objects, and thus they are more frequently reminded of the good feelings to be had in this way. Because we do not have these automatic reminders of how good our bodies can feel, it is even more important for women to make a point of learning about our bodies and what feels good to us.

There is a wonderful sense of liberation in this understanding of ourselves, for we are no longer dependent on a partner for sexual pleasure. Although chances are good that we'll still prefer sex with a partner, it is comforting to know that we can please ourselves at times when our mates are ill, on a business trip, or non-existent. Also, once we fully understand our own bodies and the kinds of stimulation we prefer, we are better able to instruct our partners on how to best please us in bed. After all, if we don't know what kinds of stimulation are most likely to bring us to orgasm, it is rather unfair to expect our partners to know.

Forty-five women said they did masturbate at some time, but only twelve of these did so frequently. As one would expect, all of the twelve were able to experience sensation, having had polio (8), cerebral palsy (3), and muscular dystrophy (1).

None regarded masturbation as a substitute for a partner but rather as an extra dimension to their sexuality. Helen Beach described it as *"just a different sexual experience—an alternative. Adds variety to one's sex life."* Scarlett, a Michigan homemaker and college student, agreed, *"It is an alternative that every person should feel comfortable with. Perhaps more open discussions on the subject should occur at every age."* Helen W. was more specific: *"When I'm not in a sexual relationship, I masturbate frequently. When I'm in one, I rarely do it alone, more with a partner but not necessarily more than intercourse."* Sounding a little like a commercial, Woodie said, *"Sometimes I don't need, want or have time with sex—masturbation is faster, easier, and a lot less messy!"* Midge, a fifty-five-year-old community relations specialist, observed [perhaps facetiously], *"It's a gap filler."*

My findings corresponded approximately with **Redbook's** survey on sexuality (Tavris and Sadd, 1977) in regard to masturbation. Although all of their participants were married (as compared with twelve of my forty-five respondents who masturbated), two-thirds masturbated and considered it a normal addition to intercourse with their husbands.

Only sixteen per cent of **Redbook's** respondents masturbated often, again about the same proportion as found in my study, but since fewer of my respondents who masturbated were married, I expected this figure in mine to be higher. There may be a clue to the reasons for this low figure, however, in the fact that of my twenty-four respondents who never masturbated, fourteen refrained from doing so for religious or moral reasons. Because Differently Abled persons live at home longer and are often regarded by parents as asexual, we may very well be overly influenced by parents' sexual taboos and be less likely to develop independent values and mores. For example, Bernice, even though separated from her husband, refused to masturbate for moral reasons and felt we should "*learn to divert sexual urges toward other interests.*" Although she did masturbate, Easy Goer revealed, "*I feel ashamed of this.*"

Of those who said they masturbated, thirty used their hands. Although there is no one "*right way*" to masturbate, only whatever is most gratifying to the individual, Rebecca Burns gave us her method as an example: "*In bed, I tickle my nipple and clitoris at the same time. Then manipulate clitoris and mouth of vagina. Rub clit vigorously at climax.*"

Other objects were much less popular for masturbation. Four women used the shower attachment on their bathroom faucets. Three women used inanimate objects such as bananas, brush handles, etc., and three others used vibrators or other mechanical gadgets like the pulsating handles of electric toothbrushes or manicure sets.

Again, only as examples and not meant to imply "*correct*" usage, two women described how they employed their vibrators.

We recall Rebecca Burns' account of using them to stretch her vagina. Continuing on the subject, she said, "*My exercise, my stretching, did not give me any special thrill, but it certainly has been psychologically gratifying....Sometimes, if I take my time and fantasize and if I rub my clitoris at the same time, I do get somewhat aroused, but I don't reach an orgasm except by rubbing my clitoris....I have enjoyed, particularly with the middle-sized ones (with the motor turned off) which I can push farther in. I have definitely found real pleasure in the sense of being filled and then moving it, especially at the same time that I manipulate my clitoris....Or, in chair, I hold fingertip on clit with Sears vibrator (turned on) on the knuckle of that finger. Or, I press vibrator down over pubic bone, over clit and down toward urethra. With vibrator on clitoris, if I persist, I may wet my pants.*" According to Lonnie Garfield Barbach (p. 107), this is common and occurs because the urethra is stimulated. She advises the Kegel exercise to strengthen the bladder muscles, urinating before masturbating, and then not letting a few drops of urine spoil one's pleasure.

Dahtee explained, "*I sent away for it* [vibrator] *and it was one of those horrid plastic type of things,...and I tried it out of desperation more than anything and really enjoyed its use,...and I later got a second one that is soft rubber compliant that I can use to enter me as well as vibrate outside. In fact, I like to use the two simultaneously, using one inside for the feel of someone inside of me and that one isn't vibrating,...and then use the other one to vibrate on the clitoris."*

A few women said they found themselves masturbating less frequently; their reasons varied. Connie L. had *"gotten so fixated on the idea that there is something wrong, due either to my disability or in addition to it, that I am afraid to explore my body or its reactions. Also I feel some discomfort which is most likely a minimal and common gynecological problem, but I'm afraid to ask. It's not as if I'm embarrassed about sex as such and certainly have no moral hangups. It's as if I have no right to sex, I'm not good enough for it."*

Again, I reiterate the importance of having gynecological examinations at regular intervals beginning at puberty, not to find out what is wrong with us but to reassure ourselves about what is **right** with us. For Connie L. to talk over her fears and discomfort with a doctor (preferably a female) would probably be helpful in diminishing them, and, of course, would give her the opportunity to seek a way of alleviating any problem that might exist.

Lola discussed qualitative differences: *"Since having polio, it takes me longer to reach orgasm on the average (often fifteen or twenty minutes). Before, it usually took about five or ten minutes. Also,...my orgasms seem weaker and/or not to last as long...,(Before polio) they were really intense, accompanied by a lot of body tensions (almost violent), and I would become almost unconscious....I'm mentioning all this because I find the differences a bit disturbing."*

Nobody else in this study has reported her orgasms to be less intense following polio. I have noticed, however, that mine, when masturbating, take longer to achieve and seem less intense now than they did when I was a teenager (the approximate age at which Lola's polio occurred). Since, even though we are Differently Abled, we are also subject to natural aging, I had attributed my gradual lessening of libido to this until I attended the recent Symposium on Polio and Aging in Chicago. There, we learned that in persons who have had polio in their early years, the aging process is often accelerated. Although sexuality was not mentioned (of course), there could be some connection, I feel. This would be a good topic for research.

Ten women seldom or never masturbated because of a lack of manual dexterity. For those of us who have this problem, vibrators are especially handy gadgets since the small ones at least are fairly light and usually can be flicked on and off easily.

Generally, in the approximate shape of a man's penis, vibrators come in many materials, textures, and sizes. As Dahtee said, some are hard plastic, others are soft and more like human skin. They may be smooth or have bumps or even spikes, supposedly for more pleasurable friction. On a recent trip to the local adult bookstore, I was amazed to see that sizes ranged from average adult penis-size to about a foot long and almost three inches in diameter, more suitable for a mare than a woman. Electrically operated vibrators are quieter than those run by batteries but are somewhat more inconvenient because of the cord. The more expensive ones have variable speeds.

They are available in bookstores featuring sexually explicit literature as well as through ads in the backs of many women's magazines. In lengths 6 3/4-12 inches, vibrators are available from Clio Living Aids, 3957 Mayfield Rd., Cleveland, Ohio 44121, and in Canada from the Shoprite Catalog Service. Attractive and discreetly mailed catalogs with all types of sexual aids are available from TXC, P.O. Box 7685, San Francisco, CA 94120, and Eve's Garden, 246 E. 51st Street, New York, NY 10022. The latter specializes in supplies designed for women.

Whether or not fantasy was important to orgasm elicited quite varying opinions. Thirteen women found it very important; twelve said it was important; and thirteen others found it totally insignificant.

Seven women said that they were much more likely to be sexually satisfied through masturbation than by their mates. April said, "*At least I know it will turn out the way I want it.*" Agreeing was Sandy Mitchell: "*I can be assured of orgasm, and a good one.*" In the earlier section on orgasm, twenty-three women cited self-stimulation as the most probable source of them. "*In terms of reliability and intensity of orgasm, I prefer masturbation,*" Lola explained, "*but intercourse is also psychologically gratifying.*"

Although three women preferred masturbation over intercourse with a partner for whom they didn't have romantic feelings, thirteen preferred to share warmth and human contact with a partner, Mary James complained that "*masturbation is so mechanical—I need T.L.C., not machines. It's a poor substitute for men but available more readily.*" Nancy stated, "*I don't know how to masturbate where I get more enjoyment from it than being with a male partner.*" Added Pamela, "*If you take the love, giving and sharing out of sex, it wouldn't mean much.*"

In view of this definite preference for a human partner, I wondered what my respondents would think of an electronic masturbating machine called a Coitron (Heslinga, pp. 189-190) being developed for possible use by Differently Abled persons who are institutionalized. Whether or not they agreed with the concept, the question spurred a large number of thought-provoking comments from respondents.

Some felt positive about it. Mae Evans exclaimed, "*Fine but why limit it to the severely disabled in an institution. If such a machine could help me have an orgasm, I'd buy it tomorrow! I think people are entitled to orgasms just as they are entitled to back rubs. Physical pleasure is healthful and feels good.*"

Carol Sea was also enthusiastic: "*I think this is about the best thing I've ever heard of, simply because if you were using some kind of thing with electrodes, the attendant could hook the person up, and either have it set on a timer or have a kind of switch device that the person could turn on or off themselves...because she/he would have the privacy incorporated. Masturbation is nice...part of the niceness of it is that it can be a private affair....I think the thing that's bothered me traditionally about things that have been professed as a solution, e.g. attendants masturbating for the patients who can't do it for themselves, it kind of sets up some altered kinds of relationships. I see the use of surrogates could be useful in this situation, but we're a long way from having that.*

"*I feel that the whole masturbation issue is very swept aside in institutions. I lived in an institution, myself, when I was younger,*" she continued, "*It used to really bother me that there were so many kids there who were not physically able to masturbate for themselves. They were pretty well ignored as sexual beings, and it was never discussed. Nobody ever tried to come up with a solution for them....It tends to be on the bottom of the priority list,*" Deena, too, empathized, "*I am all for it. I know how frustrating it can get when you need something and can't ask for help.*" Mary James added, "*I can also see its potential for sexual therapy of some disabled individuals deprived of the experience and unable to masturbate.*"

Ursula exclaimed, "*I feel that's a great idea. However, you'd never get the attendants, nurses, doctors, etc., in the institution to accept that. A great deal of education is needed before even professionals accept that handicapped persons have sexual needs, much less have the **right** to try to fulfill these needs.*"

Dahtee was "*glad that technology is able to do something that for once really helps a lot of people, and I have no qualms about it at all.*"

Many agreed that institutionalized individuals had the right to sexual relase but questioned whether Coitron would be sufficient. Michelle remarked, "*When the person to use it **wants** it, I think it's fine. But not so institutions can avoid the 'messiness' of human interaction.*" "*I'd like to try it. Why should it just be for people in institutions?*" asked Lola, "*I'm in favor of it if it works and with the stipulation that it be available at the option of a handicapped individual and not be pushed on anyone. As an only option, it is very mechanical but better than nothing.*

"*It seems to me that it would be somewhat more humane to have more prostitutes, or surrogates if you want a fancy name.*" Woodie agreed: "*I think it's a good idea if the woman is severely disabled and cannot have sex with a partner,*" (Lonnie Barbach says that physical disabilities that hinder orgasmic response in women who are able to become sexually stimulated are very rare (pp. 15-16) "*but for those people who can participate in sex to some degree with a partner and if they are confined to institutions I think they should be allowed to have the privacy to have sex with another partner if they so choose...if they are mentally capable of governing their own emotions and their own intelligences, I think that even if they are in institutions they should be allowed the opportunity to have a sexual encounter.*"

Helen W. mused, "*It's an interesting idea, but I think if I had to use one I would also need someone to attach it, and that in itself is intimate. So, I think I'd rather establish a relationship even if it were just for masturbation with someone there and make it a little more human.*" E. B. Browning said, "*Personally, I usually feel melancholy and sad after masturbating. If it was my only form of sexual release, I would not participate. I prefer someone to be near during that experience. If I was institutionalized, I would prefer male prostitutes.*"

Connie L.'s first reaction was "*to picture a horrible 1984, chrome and glass universe in which everyone is a functioning organism unto himself but no longer a person....I would like to see severely disabled people able to make more contact with the other people living with them as well as with the able-bodied people who would be working or visiting there. Even severely disabled people should be able to have some sort of sexual life. There are lots of things to be done besides just intercourse...and although the awkward fumbling might be less technically effi-*

cient than the Coitron, I think the experience of being touched physically and emotionally by another human being would more than make up for the imperfection."

"When I first read it," said Martha Merriweather, *"I thought that's great....However, after thinking about it for a while, the thought occurred to me that if there wasn't already a feeling of emotional deprivation or if there were, it would either be accentuated or come into being where it hadn't been before. Sex, in and of itself, without love and warmth from another human being, would tend to leave an emptiness and a need unfulfilled that would lead to frustration, I think."*

Anet raised a slightly different issue: *"If it's truly a masturbating machine, I get the idea that masturbating is done alone although I realize that it's not, but usually it's thought of as being alone with your own fantasies. I wonder if a person could succeed in doing that within the environment of an institution."*

Surprisingly, Jennifer thought that sexual release would not be a problem for the Differently Abled living in institutions: *"I don't see where really disabled persons confined to an institution would need a sexual outlet, and especially if they had never experienced sex before, it seems like it would be dormant and that it wouldn't need to be satisfied...."* This study does not support Jennifer's thesis. Over and over, we have seen that one does not have to have prior sexual experience in order to feel sexual urges. The need for sexual release is a natural instinct just like the need for food and sleep. A newborn baby does not have to eat before she cries out to be nursed.

Although thirty-six women only masturbated alone, masturbation is increasingly being considered another form of sex play to be done with a partner. In a recent discussion with a former lover, he revealed that one of his most sexually satisfying experiences occurred when he held a woman and sucked her breasts while she masturbated. Barbach (pp. 152-153) includes masturbation with a partner present in the exercise sequence she advocated to teach women to be orgasmic with their partners, for in this way partners can learn how the women prefer to be touched. Six women did usually masturbate with a partner. In fact, Samantha said, *"I have never masturbated without a partner present."*

"I am still trying to learn to masturbate properly," said Penny S. This is unfortunate because there is no *"proper"* way. Genitals, men's and women's, are as unique as faces. Betty Dodson in her

book, *Liberating Masturbation: A Meditation on Self Love*, beautifully illustrates many variations of female sex organs, all of which are considered "*normal*." (As the title implies, this little book is very helpful in freeing one of inhibitions about masturbating and can be ordered for $5.00 from Dodson, P.O. Box 1933, New York, NY 10116.)

Thinking of all the different smiles of pleasure we have witnessed so far in our lifetime can give us some idea of the great variety of individual sexual responses. Most of us don't value a boistrous laugh more than a shy smile but recognize that each is a personal response to a specific stimulus at a certain point in time. What may trigger a face-splitting grin at one time, may, at another, result in a mere twitch of the facial muscles, depending on mood, health, or a host of other circumstances. If we could learn to accept and appreciate sexual responses, our own and others', without criticism or comparisons, the way we do smiles, we would all be more sexually healthy. Not only would our individual response during masturbation intensify as we increasingly learn to accept ourselves but our sexual relationships with partners would also be enhanced.

The book I've been referring to throughout this chapter, *For Yourself: The Fulfillment of Female Sexuality* by Lonnie Garfield Barbach, contains much more helpful information on all of this than I could possibly give, and I recommend it to any women wishing to fully develop herself as a sexual being. A quality paperback costing $4.95, it is in most bookstores that have comprehensive women's sections. Published by Anchor Books, a division of Doubleday in Garden City, New York, it can probably also be ordered from them. Happy Discovering!

13

Womyn Loving Womyn (Lesbianism)

When I was a child, my parents rented out upstairs rooms to a couple of women named Jenny and Marie, working women, probably in their thirties. Sometimes after dinner, Marie, the strong one, would carry me upstairs where they would play music for me and give me cookies; I loved them. Then, one day, I heard my mother telling my father in secretive tones that she thought they "*were queer.*" I thought they were more fun than most of the adults I knew and didn't understand at all when I was no longer allowed to go upstairs for my evening visits.

Homosexuality is virtually out of the closet now, and today, I would probably have had some inkling of what my mother meant. A friend recently told me she overheard one nine-year-old boy call another a "*homo*". Lesbianism is freely discussed, within the general population now, and it appears that more women are becoming practicing lesbians, although it may only be that people are becoming more open about sexual preferences.

I wondered if the women in my study would have opportunities to explore this avenue of sexuality as freely as other women. Forty-four women said they had never been approached sexually by another woman. Twenty-four had only been approached once or twice, with just three having frequent opportunities for sexual contact with other women.

A different three women felt that they had received more advances

155

because of their specific physical condition. Brillig thought she was *"approached more by my own sex because I am disabled. I feel doomed...exasperated...like maybe they know something I don't...like maybe tomorrow I'll be that way, and then I can have a sex life. But tomorrow never comes. I think they wouldn't hate me for my sexuality, which men do...unfortunately I'm attracted to men."* Rebecca Burns said, *"The subject of lesbian relations is extremely troubling to me. I have a strong sense of taboo. Yet all my close friendships and opportunities have been with **females**. I blame this on my disability."* Most felt that their contacts were either less because they were Differently Abled (17) or about the same.

.Their reactions to the idea of having sexual contact initiated by other women were mixed depending on whether or not they had experienced this. Thirteen women either did not want to be approached or had been and rejected it. Amy Bradburn, a thirty-year-old nurse from Illinois, said, *"The whole thing turns me off."* Ten other women felt as Ursula did. *"Homosexuality is not my thing but each to his own."*

Four expressed a strong sense of taboo against lesbianism which seemed to be linked to their being Differently Abled. Linda said she *"used to be afraid that people would think I was lesbian because of my disability."* They saw it as an additional stigma to those already possessed (being a woman and Differently Abled).

The reactions of seven women were definitely positive. Penny S. confided, *"I would like to have a full sexual relationship with a woman, but I am very shy about this feeling. I hope I meet an understanding woman someday."* Connie L. said, that although her *"orientation seems to be towards males, I wouldn't mind giving it a try with the right person under the right circumstances."* Nancy did not see herself *"having a lesbian relationship at this point in my life, but that's not to say I never will. Very open to the idea."* Agreeing, Summer *"would not feel free to have one though until I am confident with myself as a heterosexual person. I do not want to feel that I chose homosexuality as a second resort. I would like to experience more for the emotional rewards rather than the physical—I would want to have a homosexual relationship with a woman I love."*

Fifty-nine women had never had any sexual contact with women. Eight had encountered it once or twice. Rebecca Burns described, *"First, when I was ten, a girlfriend placed her hands over my breasts. I was aroused, frightened, said 'Don't!' and she took them away. When I was eighteen, the same girl kissed me on the neck. We were both aroused but afraid to continue.*" Her experience was pretty typical; five respondents had received this kind of contact from school friends. One had been initiated by a family member.

Although five women had found these exploratory lesbian experiences very pleasurable, two said that they were not at all likely to repeat them. Whether or not they enjoyed it at all, most did not plan on continuing this mode of sexuality.

Three women who found their initial lesbian experiences very pleasurable said that they **were** very likely to continue them. Daisy D. felt "*rapport is what counts! Clitoris or penis—just skin. When love and respect and consent and opportunity is there, why leave any beloved one out,*" adding, "*I'm newly somewhat Bi.*" Anet agreed, "*Humanoids...I'd like to feel free to integrate sex into my life...make love with my friends when affection takes us to those feelings.*"

Twenty-three women did not feel that other women would be more understanding of their situations than men. Jay Kirfirst felt that she was "*not permitted* [by able-bodied women] *to take part in adult or sex discussions.*" Jane Grant perceived she was "*at times treated in a motherly fashion.*" Nine women thought they would be treated better in sexual situations than they would be by men, and fifteen were unsure. Anet found, "*Women of the women's movement are receptive. Other women tend to see me as an embittered cripple.*"

How do women treat other women? Are women more understanding of each other's specific physical condition in sexual situations? To find out the answers to these and related questions, I revised the original questionnaire and arranged to have twenty copies distributed at the first Disabled Lesbian Conference held in August, 1981, following the Women's Music Festival at Hesperia, Michigan. Although the two responses returned can in no way be considered definitive, they do give some clues about what it is like to be a Differently Abled lesbian in today's world. I am grateful to both Jane and Ruth for their candor.

Jane, an art therapist in New York, is thirty-three. She has amyotonia congenita and uses a motorized wheelchair. She received her elementary education through home teaching, with no sex education, of course. As a child, she had virtually no voice in choosing clothes or hairstyles and little more as a teenager. Denying her sexuality, Jane's parents gave her dual messages—that she "*was just like everyone else but not good enough, or I was very disabled (no expectations).*" Nevertheless, as a child, she retained a fairly positive self-image; this faded, however, as a teenager. For a time, she "*rejected my disability which was part of me; therefore, I rejected me.*"

She is now coming to the realization that her "*struggle is more about being a woman than being disabled....Society rejects disabled but will take care of them; society rejects lesbians and may destroy them.*" Passionate about survival in a hostile world, she is "*concerned with the rape of women, rape of lesbians, rape of the earth—trying to defend against the rape of my soul by loving and nurturing a little piece of land which can harbor women through the oncoming storm.*"

Both Jane and Ruth had heterosexual relationships before acknowledging their homosexual tendencies. Of her first lesbian affair, Jane said, "*I fell in love with my roommate (a lesbian) and ex-aide....My love for her put me in touch with earlier fantasies and wishes about other women friends, teachers, etc. She was pre-orgasmic and afraid to try to let me satisfy her—frustrated both of us. We broke up. No support in lesbian community for her dealing with my disability. Women looked down on her and thought it weird just because we were roommates.*"

"*Coming out*" is a term used by lesbians to indicate the time when they openly acknowledge their sexual preference, no longer trying to hide it from family and friends. Jane described her experience in coming out: "*I was concerned about aides' attitudes and whether women would want me (same fears about men wanting me).*

"*Parents, angry, rejected me—Dad didn't speak to me for several months. Now they pretend they don't know.*"

Jane is growing to "*feel adequate and satisfied—still reaching but for my ideals, not theirs.*" A talented artist and writer, she considered herself a radical feminist revolutionary as well as a disabled lesbian and healer.

Jane was instrumental in organizing the first Disabled Lesbian Conference, which Ruth, a thirty-five-year-old psychologist, said, "*began a networking process which has left me with the feeling that I have friends—disabled women—all across the country. This is vastly comforting to me and reduces my sense of isolation.*"

Ruth has epilepsy which began when she was ten years old and is partially paralyzed on the right side of her body.

Her parents "*were terrified of* [her specific physical condition] *and remain so—unable to use the word, 'seizure'. They re-*

sponded oversolicitously and with obvious discomfort when seizures happened—then denied the condition between times. I learned to do the same. None of us knew any better."

Consequently, Ruth also acquired a negative self-concept, viewing herself when an adolescent as "*ugly, fat, with no sense of humor, no creativity, and totally unlikable. How one acquired friends became a total mystery. My extremely high I.Q. was the only resource I felt I had so I devoted all my energy there. As an adult, I have had to integrate all those 'cut off' parts. I have spent much time accepting my physical self and learning to have trust in it the way I do my intellect....My emotional self is still a bit cut off.*

Ruth "*came out*" thirteen years ago when she was "*still massively denying the epilepsy....Coming out was one of the most life-giving actions I have ever taken and only occurred after many previous stages to regain emotional health. The woman I was with had had a friend with epilepsy in childhood. She was practical, calm, and unruffled by the seizures. She, through her example of acceptance, helped me to begin to accept.*

"*Being a lesbian feels like the essence of womynliness in my heart. To love other womyn seems a natural, right, and beautiful manner in which to express myself as a female person. Being disabled mostly just hurts, and there seems no natural connection with either my status as womyn or lesbian.*"

"*My parents were vehemently against my lesbianism. It has only been through much struggle on all our parts that we are able to accept each other better and can realize how much we love one another. This has taken thirteen years of work. They are uncomfortable with my friends, but we continue to grow.*"

Ruth's specific physical condition, at the time of her response, was causing her some problems in expressing herself sexually. She explained, "*I now have considerable difficulty with sexuality with lesbians, although I have been 'out' for thirteen years, due to fears that a seizure may occur during sex (it has) and the sleepiness caused by (anti-convulsant) drugs which make sex at night almost impossible. I don't want to be seen naked having a seizure....Occasional incontinence is especailly hard. Jokes about my sleeping...or being spacy hurt.*

"*It's hard for me to trust my bodily self enough to 'let go' so it's often hard to reach orgasm even though I get extremely aroused. I worry that my partner is getting tired, bored, or frustrated. Sometimes I tell* [her] *to stop, or they say they are tired. Sometimes I masturbate to climax. I don't 'fake it' anymore.*

Almost always feel inadequate, wrong, as if I am 'a problem'...have opted to have no contact for the last eighteen months. I now want to reconnect but am still frightened."

Like Jane, Ruth is an advocate for change. "*Over the past decade, I have been extremely active politically in the gay community doing CR* [consciousness raising] *groups, therapy, public speaking, appearing on radio and T.V., educating other mental health professionals. My goal has been to reduce homophobia and sexism through exposure and education as well as to lobby politically for increased civil rights."*

From their separate spheres of influence, Jane and Ruth discussed their level of comfort with the lesbian community in comparison with the straight. Jane felt less accepted because "*lesbian community values physical strength. Oppressed women (lesbians) are reluctant to take on another oppression (my disability). Lesbians more able to accept me now than four years ago because I am now a 'famous disabled lesbian.' I am, however, still disabled—now they all know me, but they don't share about themselves to me."*

Jane's observations are particularly revealing in view of the fears earlier in this chapter of a few respondents who thought they might be considered lesbian because they were Differently Abled. For one thing, it indicates to me that their fears were probably unfounded. More significant, and saddening, however, is that each group feels so stigmatized that its members cannot risk the greater pain that might result if we were to unequivocally accept and trust each other as women.

Ruth, whose specific physical conditon is much less visible than Jane's felt "*more accepted by the lesbian community probably because that is where I am most comfortable. I have gained considerable respect for my therapeutic expertise among the mental health community but am not usually very comfortable in social settings with many of these people."* She perceived that she is seen by other lesbians "*as a lesbian with a strong liking for women's culture, with an interest in our herstory, present and future possibilities....The degree of ableism I encounter is about the same in both communities."*

Ruth's perceptions of being seen more positively than Jane did by other lesbians correspond to my findings regarding heterosexual women. In my main study, the more obvious the specific physical condition, the less likely other women were to see my respondents

160

as sexual beings. Of the fifteen women who felt they were viewed as asexual by other women, ten either used wheelchairs or were Differently Abled in otherwise visible ways.

Apparently, it is easier for both sexes to think of a very Differently Abled woman as a sexual being if there is no possibility of her becoming that person's sexual partner; of the eleven women who felt they were seen by men as asexual, nine either used wheelchairs or had other obvious specific physical conditons.

It is interesting to note that the activities both women listed as making them feel more womanly were with only a few exceptions identical to those listed by the heterosexual women in my study.

Ruth said, "*Oddly enough, it's been reclaiming an ability to do some of the traditional activities of women such as cooking and entertaining. When in woman-identified spaces, i.e., Michigan Women's Music Festival....Visiting women friends and having dinner with them. Sometimes during therapy when there is a need to nurture a person through an especially painful time. Playing with children. When I am physically affectionate or sexual with women. Exploring being a sister to my siblings and a daughter to my father.*"

Things that made Jane feel more womanly were again, cooking, as well as "*making love, giving support, working, exploring myself sensually (allowing my hair to grow, sleeping naked), dancing in my chair, being alone when I can.*"

From the findings here, as well as through reading and personal friendships with some lesbians in the past few years, I can only conclude that none of us are very different. All of us want to be accepted and loved for what we are inside. Any loving, sexual relationship with another person, male or female, is difficult in today's society and requires infinite amounts of patience and attention to survive and grow. Even though it might be argued that a woman better understands another woman, there are still plenty of hereditary, environmental, cultural, and just plain old personality differences that make lesbian relationships just as challenging as heterosexual ones. A Differently Abled woman might opt for lesbianism, just as other women do, because of her own needs and desires, but she would be mistaken if she did so, expecting liaisons to be easier to form or maintain.

I do feel that lesbian women, as a whole, are making much more of a sincere effort to understand and include us in their publications and programs than are straight women's groups. An outstanding example of providing for our special needs with creative energy and enthusiasm is the already mentioned Women's Music Festival in Michigan.

A small, but seemingly comprehensive book entitled **Sapphistry: The Book of Lesbian Sexuality** by Pat Califia (1980) contains a short but sensitive discussion of issues we face such as accessibility and body image, followed by short summaries of the major Differently Abling conditions which include anything that could affect sexuality. **Off Our Backs**, a lesbian periodical, devoted an entire issue to Differently Abled women earlier this year and frequently contains contributions from writers with specific physical conditions.

I see few similar examples of attempts to bridge the gap between us by the heterosexual women's movement, whose members often do not understand the real issues we face. Mary James, in explaining why she did not feel part of the women's movement, remarked that at the same time they were so concerned about whether or not they should have to make coffee for their bosses, she could probably not even get into the building nor be able to "*lift the damn coffeepot!*"

14

Where Are We Going, and How Will We Get There? (Now It's Your Turn)

Attitudes and images, ours and others', and the ways they affect us have been a recurrent theme throughout this book. In this final chapter, I will take one last look at Differently Abled women in the latter part of the twentieth century. What can we do to support one another as we strive for self-actualization? How do we handicap ourselves and each other? What is our role in the women's movement? How do we fit into society as a whole?

I recently received in the mail a paper entitled "Disabled Women: Sexism Without the Pedestal" (Fine and Asch, 1981) in which the term, "rolelessness" is used to describe the status of Differently Abled women in society. Whereas Differently Abled men have the choice of identifying either with their disability or with their maleness—a more positive image—according to the authors, women have no real option, since both identities are seen as equally powerless. To what extent is this true?

Because of her specific physical condition (systemic lupus), Dahtee sometimes must use a wheelchair and at other times can walk unassisted; from this unique vantage point, she has been able to study how the same persons' attitudes toward her changed according to whether she was Differently Abled or able-bodied: *"Before I was disabled, I was always very popular...very strong personality, infectious laugh, good listener as well as a good*

163

talker, and I knew how people responded to me then....And then, when I was disabled, I went through these amazing realizations of how people treat disabled people....I was always so used to people being respectful of my intelligence and my knowledge, and suddenly, I had people leaning down and slowly articulating into my face, 'Are you all right, dear?' type of things....I was not allowed to be respected....I did not feel that anybody could see any of the beauty in me."

With nothing else changed but her legs' physical ability to carry her around, Dahtee's status vacillated between that of a pretty, well-educated, young woman and a mentally impaired illiterate. She was fortunate in possessing a strong sense of self. For those of us whose egos may not have been so fully developed when we became Differently Abled or who have faced this kind of oppression since early childhood, finding suitable roles is bound to be more difficult, however. For example, Connie L. stated, *"I have no role in society and feel really rotten about it...this is perhaps the hardest and most devastating question...because it has forced me to confront myself and how I have allowed myself to diminish to a point where I hardly feel I exist anymore."*

Anet emphasized that we must make an effort toward self-determination: *"One thing that is disturbing to me is how easy it is for people with disabilities to give up their right to make their own decisions and to control their own lives. Somehow, we are convinced very early in our disability, whether the disability occurs to us as a child or in mid-adulthood,...that we are totally dependent, helpless, and this is just not true....*

"Eight years of isolation in San Francisco," she continued, *"taught me how easy it is to get into an attitude of helplessness, of just deciding that there is no cure for the situation of isolation. It takes a lot more aggressiveness and assertiveness than we really want to have, to get out and be a member of society, to find answers for our needs. They just don't exist at home....If I want to take a class in art, I should be able to do that and not just say, 'Well, it's too much of a hassle to cope with transportation getting there....' We just have to fight the ease with which we can slip into an apathetic state, so it entails changes in behavior patterns that many times create problems."*

There is an interesting parallel here in the dependent wife who relies on her husband to make all her decisions, to supply her with opinions on all major issues, and, in fact, to define her world for her. Sanctioned by a large segment of society, this cocoon type of existence becomes more and more comfortable as one relinquishes her mind and heart to the control of another, and this can be a very difficult mold from which to break away.

Taking responsibility for one's own life is risky; one may make poor decisions and have to live with them without shifting blame to anyone else; one may be faced with tremendous challenges, physically, mentally, and spiritually.

What are the rewards? To determine one's own existence can be exciting. This book could never have been written, for example, if, twelve years ago, I had not relinquished my easy, dependent existence with an aunt and uncle to try living independently in Ann Arbor. It has not been easy, and I still don't feel quite as self-determining as Colleen Moore, a California paraplegic, who said, "*I know I can create the events of my life as I wish.*" But I continue to grow more self-reliant even as my physical abilities weaken, because independence is a state of mind, not a state of body, and even my worst days, are better than those comfortable eons I passed doing nothing more strenuous than crocheting and watching T.V.

Do we take a back seat to Differently Abled men? Thinking back over the years to the numerous committees, boards, task forces, etc., on which I have served with other Differently Abled persons, the most vocal, the most assertive, the most adamant about the need for change, I recall, have been women. This trend appears to be continuing in the younger generation; one of my helpers, who served at a camp for Differently Abled children last summer, observed that the female children were usually the most assertive.

Women have emerged as early leaders in the struggle for equality waged by other minorities. Harriet Tubman and other black women who risked their lives daily so that others could take the Underground Railroad to freedom come first to mind. Perhaps those who suffer double oppression are first to recognize the necessity of liberation and, being already at the bottom of the totem pole, have the least to risk by speaking against the system.

As many of us become leaders and spokeswomen in our movement for equal rights, what can we do to support each other as we all seek the roles, traditional or non-traditional, best suited to us? Anet and Lola expressed their thoughts on this subject:

"*There really needs to be more thought put into how disabled people can become independent,*" Anet said. "*And there has to be more discussion of philosophy of independence that is not connected at all with the number of things a person has to be dependent upon. That is, independence really starts within you....*

"*I've known many attendant/disabled person relationships*

that I would call very unsatisfactory because the disabled person doesn't think of the attendant as an employee but...as a caretaker or parent figure, getting back to the opposition between philosophies of self-reliance and caretaking. These are two philosophies that are directed at the disabled, and I don't think [she] *is getting enough of the self-reliance philosophy....*

"We need to counsel newly disabled and children who are disabled on self-reliance and decision-making in evaluating where we are in life and what our status is in connection with the rest of society and learning how to improve it."

Lola *"would like to see more handicapped people in the various media, more active, less stereotyped portrayal...not just as main characters but also...supporting roles, bit parts—how about a handicapped secretary or neighbor, a handicapped woman sitting in a bar or restaurant that the main character walks into.*

"Also, it has occurred to me that I've never seen a handicapped person on a game show. Do they think we don't like money?...I've never seen anyone handicapped doing a commercial. We buy all that stuff too."

Certainly, economic pressure is a valid tool, used with varying success by other minorities. Two things are important to remember when boycotting products and services to protest discrimination. First, sufficient numbers of persons must participate in order to make a financial impact; so it is a good idea to enlist the support of relatives, friends, and classmates, etc. Second, the proprietors should be informed of the reasons you and others are boycotting them as well as the changes you expect them to make.

How do we further handicap each other in our mutual struggle for full acceptance? Although stereotyping, a natural strategy we all use to put some order into a chaotic world, does not have to be prejudicial, it all too often locks us into others' expectations of us. It is essential that we examine our own attitudes regarding persons with other specific physical conditions to be sure that we are not hindering them from attaining their full potential.

Dahtee related her growth in self-awareness upon suddenly becoming Differently Abled: *"I remember being just amazed when I realized my own stereotypes and my own prejudices against disabled people. That was the greatest learning experience for me when...I realized that...here I was sitting in a wheelchair with my own personal problems, and I knew nothing about the deaf world, I knew nothing about the blind world—cerebral palsy scared me to death—wouldn't allow myself to give them the intelligence that I so wanted people to give me."*

She went on to explain how her world expanded as she overcame her bigotry: *"I've gotten very involved with sign language, in going for my certification as an interpreter because one of the men that I met and became sweethearts with was a deaf man...so I began using sign on a daily level for communication...because I was seeing him all the time, and I began to really respect this beautiful language system, with the beautiful, honest concepts and grammar—everything about it."*

Patting ourselves on the back because we are farther along the road to independence than others with similar specific physical conditions is a form of snobbery we can all do without, for, certainly, in diminishing the accomplishments of others, we diminish ourselves. Expressing how she felt about this tendency was Rebecca Burns: *"I bitterly hate the feeling of stigma I have among other handicapped people because I live with my mother. I feel that they think I'm backward, and I hate the feeling of having less confidence in some ways than some of my peers."*

Several respondents felt alienated from the women's movement. Having suffered more serious discrimination as a result of being Differently Abled than being women, they thought that most feminists neither understood nor even acknowledged this problem. Mary James said, *"Disabled women are the symbol of the most major form of 'oppressed people' in this country, but I don't feel the women's movement is doing any recognizing of this. I am definitely a feminist but have no allegiance with women's groups. Their...problems seem so trivial as compared to those of the disabled women."* Michelle felt *"left out....I am a feminist—radical probably—but I see that as a separate part of my life from disability...there is no arm of the movement concerned about disabled women." "We do fit in,"* remarked Deena, *"but only on the outside like some sort of mascot."*

Personally, I feel that there is little genuine concern displayed for Differently Abled women except by some lesbians in the women's movement. Besides being more conscious of the sexual myths and taboos that can hurt us all, lesbians often seem more politically aware of other minority movements than other feminists. The Michigan Women's Music Festival stands as an illustration of how we can be accommodated at meetings and gatherings with minimal financial expense when planners are sensitive to our needs and creative about meeting them.

The following women discussed the discrimination we face and how they felt the women's movement was benefiting us:

Connie L. described the evolution of her thinking about our relationship to the women's movement: *"At first, though I've always considered myself a supporter of the feminist movement, I felt rather isolated from it. I could understand their outrage at being judged wholly or primarily on the basis of their sex, but my problem was having people recognize that I had a sex.*

"As time went on though, I felt disabled women fit well into the women's movement. The need to fit into a particular mold in order to be considered a 'real woman' was lessened by the movement...a sensitizing of men, a reevaluation of what they considered important in a woman and a relationship, couldn't help but make life better for disabled women. And, of course, the more wide open the choice of life styles, the better it is for us highly 'irregular' types; so I think disabled women could not only benefit from the changes but have a lot to offer in helping to bring them about."

Jenny Jones, a paraplegic since birth, spoke, *"We, in a way, have a double problem. Once you buck the disability, then you're next bucking the fact that you're a woman. I don't think I've had the discrimination because I'm a woman because they never saw beyond the disability, which may also be the factor in the fact that they don't know you."*

Added Martha Merriweather, *"We have to fight architectural barriers, attitudinal barriers, employment barriers...in addition to all that, we're also women. I think this takes a great deal of endurance, stamina, determination, but I intend to pursue it to the best of my abilities. I have wondered when I receive my degree in journalism, where I will go from there. Will I be accepted even though I am handicapped? I would hope that my personality is strong enough, that my skills are sharp enough,...that I am going to get the job that I want when the time comes."*

Carol Sea, a social worker, thought the women's movement had been especially beneficial to us by helping others *"realize that individuals should do the jobs that they are best at doing rather than doing jobs that they think they are supposed to do. In other words, because of the shift in the emphasis of women being homemakers,...in my relationship with my partner, I can go out and earn money at an intellectual job...and my partner could stay home and do the manual stuff."*

Mae Evans summarized, *"Before I was disabled, I had a comfortable identity as a wife, mother, and community leader....I thought 'women's rights' were for others who had not lucked into a good life situation. After paraplegia, things were different. I lost my comfortable identity because I could no longer function in that role. I had to find some other way to operate, but there was no other way because I was no longer able to do the things that a female person 'does' to be worthwhile. When I went into therapy for post-paraplegia depression, I became angry that the depression was not caused by the leg loss; it was caused by my original low self-esteem which prevented me from accepting leg loss. I discovered that I had been a victim of cultural attitudes on women and didn't even know it.*

"Disabled women can learn from the women's movement how they have been held back by things other than their own disabilites. We may not be able to improve our personal physical situation, but we can change how we and others feel about our being women."

Reciprocal relationships in which we are able to give as well as receive are generally more satisfying, and this is no less so in our liaison with the women's movement. Pooh Grayson noted, *"Disabled women are good problem-solvers, good managers, and have endless determination, or they don't survive. Those of us who have made a life of our own would be a great asset to the women's movement."*

Mae Evans went a step further: *"Able-bodied women can learn from the disabled, who have had to learn this before they can truly cope, that the physical body is not as important as the person who lives inside; that one is first, a person and second, a female; that sex is less important than sexuality, and individuality is more important than these two; and that every woman who is honestly involved in her own personal growth is making a contribution to the women's movement whether she is aware of it or not."*

What were the major concerns of the Differently Abled women in this study? Certainly, the desires they expressed, financial and emotional security, sexual happiness, barrier-free access to the community, and legal rights, are no different than those of most able-bodied women. Overwhelming all other concerns throughout this book, however, even when they appeared to be talking about something else, has been the need to be fully accepted as women rather than as asexual objects of pity. *"I am new in the community...,and I'm also newly married,"* Sally Smith said. *"One of my bigger concerns is that I be accepted as one of the housewives...rather than a poor disabled female...I do not want this type of concern/sympathy, and I find it very difficult to become one of the girls. In fact, it has been impossible so far....I would like to be more a person—me, Sally Smith, the person—rather than me, that poor girl in the wheelchair."*

"First and foremost," stressed Woodie, *"I want people to know that I'm a person regardless of whether I have a disability. I have wants and needs and fears; I'm happy and I'm sad just like anybody else. I'm not immune to feelings and because I do have feelings I am a person....*

"Secondly, I'm a woman. I do consider myself liberated—if not physically liberated, legally liberated,...spiritually liberated. Being a woman is very important to me....

"Last but by no means least, I am a disabled woman. That also brings with it a few added concerns, but my disability is not the biggest most important thing in my life. I do not want people to judge me simply because I am disabled."

Woodie would probably agree with Martha Merriweather who said, *"I love people who accept me for what I am—people who forget the fact that I'm in a wheelchair and will bring a chair to the table at dinner for me and then apologize and say, 'Oh gee, I forgot.' I find that extremely complimentary."*

Indeed it is. My ideal person will do whatever is necessary to help me function independently, then, will forget about my specific physical condition and treat me as me—lover, friend, writer, or whatever I am in relation to that person.

When **we** can forget about being Differently Abled, I am convinced that it helps others to do so. Forgetting about it does not mean being passive or giving up the fight for accessible buildings and transportation, equal opportunities for employment, and legal rights. On the contrary, we must become even more assertive about obtaining these; having them will render us more independent and, thus, make it easier to concentrate on others rather than on ourselves and our limitations. Being more creative in finding new methods of doing things may help us forget about it for longer periods of time. Becoming better organized in daily activities may mean less time with an attendant; everyone needs some time alone every day to think and dream.

Most of all, forgetting the specific physical condition does not mean ignoring or failing to accept its existence. The period of solitude each day is particularly essential in truly coming to grips with it, for in really accepting the limitations, whatever they may be, while still striving to realize one's full endowment lies the key to full personhood.

Becoming a full person and not just *"a poor girl"* is not easy; it takes a lot of effort, but then most worthwhile achievements do. In closing, Elizabeth Mark and Deena gave us a glimpse of the rewards:

Elizabeth Mark: *"I love so much, There is not much I hate. Maybe other women who are disabled will realize, as I did, that there is love in our world—you just have to push yourself to your potential."*

Deena: *"I don't have any more hates since I just made the miraculous discovery that I accept myself as what I am, and I am loved more for the right reasons because of this discovery."*

I'm A Woman

Chorus: I'm a Woman
So let me tell you about me
(Sisters)
When you know all there is to know 'bout me
(Sisters)
Then you will know why everybody has to be free
(Talking to my sisters)

        If I'd been born a man
        I might have been to war
        And they'd buy me a car
        A guitar, a star
        A hero I might be
        But as you can plainly see

Chorus: I'm a woman
Not one of many, but few
(Sisters)
Not exactly like any number of you
(Sisters)
Still I know full well that it's got to be true
(Talking to my sisters)

        If I'd been born a man
        I might have had the right
        To work that pays enough
        A citizen I would be
        But as you can clearly see

Chorus: I'm a Woman
I've tried to tell you about me
(Sisters)
Now you know all there is to know about me
(Sisters)
And you know why everybody has to be free
(Sisters)
(Talking to my sisters)

Tall Enough to Stand

Anna was born without any arms
The product of an experimental craze
But Anna was born a woman with hope inside her heart
And no disability will keep her in a cage
For she is a warrior in a great revolution
And every war has got its casualties
No you don't need an athlete to make an amazon
And you don't need sight to see the possibilities

Nicki was born a fine & healthy baby
So active she was less than well behaved
But at the age of twenty-one
Her dying had begun
Congenital disease would take her to an early grave
Yet she is a warrior in a great revolution
Disabled at the patriarchy's hand
No you don't need an athlete to make an amazon
And you don't need legs to be tall enough to stand

Rene was born in complete and utter silence
And living in total silence she remains
But Rene was born a womon with spirit in her bones
And no disability will bring her any shame
For she is a warrior in a great revolution
And every war has got it's casualties
No you don't need an athlete to make an amazon
And you don't need sight to see the possibilities

For we are the warriors in this great revolution
Disabled in an abled bodied land
No you don't need an athlete to make an amazon
And you don't need legs to be tall enough
Oh, be tall enough to stand

GLOSSARY

Definitions

Amyotonia Congentia
Lack of muscular tone; floppiness and weakness in infancy due to a variety of causes

Arthritis
Inflammation of a joint(s), local or widespread

Arthrogryposis
Retention of a joint in a fixed position due to muscular contraction and other causes

Atrophy
An acquired local reduction in the size of a cell, tissue, organ, or region of the body

Cerebral Palsy
Congenital brain damage resulting in motor disability

Cystostomy
In surgery, the formation of an opening into the urinary bladder wall

Dildo
Penis shaped object used for genial stimulation

Epilepsy
Chronic nerve disorder resulting from recurring surge "discharges"

Hemiplegia
Paralysis to one-half (lateral) of the body, may involve loss of speech, as a result of injury or disease

Hyperesthesia
Increased sensitivity of the skin to tactile, painful, thermal, and other stimuli

Multiple Sclerosis
Usually progressive degeneration of myelin sheath surrounding central nervous system

Muscular Dystrophy
Usually progressive degeneration of muscle fibers and replacement by fatty and fibrous tissue

Myasthenia Gravis
Easily fatigued and weakened muscles especially of eyes, throat, and respiratory areas

Orgasm
Intense, diffuse, and subjectively pleasurable sensation experienced during sexual intercourse or genital manipulation, culminating for the male in ejaculation and for the female, in

	uterine contractions and pelvic throbbing sensations
Os	Any mouth or opening into the body or body part
Ovulation	Maturation and discharge of an egg cell which is capable of developing into an embryo with fertilization
Paraplegia	Paralysis of lower limbs, with possible loss of control of bowel and bladder, as a result of injury or disease
Poliomyelitis	Viral infection of spinal cord, accompanied by muscle atrophy and weakness of involved limbs
Quadriplegia	Total paralysis of lower limbs with total or partial paralysis of upper limbs, with possible loss of bowel and bladder control as well as restricted respiratory function, as a result of injury or disease
Semen	Fluid produced by the male reproductive organs, carrying the sperm, or male germ cells
Scoliosis	Lateral curvature of the spine
Spastic	Pertaining to continuous spasms; extremely tense, easily agitated, anxious
Sperm	One of the mature germ (egg) cells of the male; used interchangeably with semen
Spina Bifida	A congenital defect in the closure of the vertebral canal with a protrusion of a portion of the spinal cord
Systemic Lupus Erythematous	A disease characterized by changes in the body's connective tissue which involves primarily the kidney, spleen, skin, and heart. It can be accompanied by fevers, muscle and joint pains, anemia, and frequently by skin eruptions
Thrombophlebitis	Inflammation of a vein associated with a clot of blood formed during life within the vessel
Urinostomy	See cystostomy
Werdnig-Hoffman Syndrome	Infantile spinal muscular atrophy

176

Bibliography

Asch, Adrienne and Fine, Michelle (1981) Disabled Women: Sexism Without the Pedestal Unpublished Paper, University of Pennsylvania.

Barbach, Lonnie Garfield (1976) *For Yourself: The Fulfillment of Female Sexuality* Anchor Press, Garden City, N.Y.

Baxter, Robert T. (Fall, 1981) Divorce—The Second Trauma. *Accent on Living*, 26:2

Boston Women's Health Book Collective (1976) *Our Bodies, Ourselves:* A Book By and For Women, 2nd ed. Simon and Schuster, New York.

Burden, R.L. (1980) Measuring the Effects of Stress on the Mothers of Handicapped Infants: Must Depression Always Follow? *Child Care, Health and Development*, 6:2

Buscaglia, Leo (1975) *The Disabled and Their Parents: A Counseling Challenge* Charles B. Slack, Inc., Thorofare, NJ.

_____ (1972) *Love*: A Warm and Wonderful Book about the Largest Experience in Life Fawcett Crest Books, New York.

Califia, Pat (1980) *Sapphistry: The Book of Lesbian Sexuality* The Naiad Press, Inc., Tallahassee, FL.

Cappaert, Lael (1961) *And God Said No* Augustana Press, Rock Island, IL.

Colgrove, Melba, Ph.D., Bloomfield, Harold H., M.D. and McWilliams, Peter (1976) *How to Survive the Loss of a Love*: 58 Things to Do When There is Nothing To Be Done. Simon and Schuster, New York.

Delaney, Janice, Lupton, Mary Jane and Toth, Emily (1976) *The Curse*: A Cultural History of Menstruation E.P. Dutton and Co., Inc., New York.

Dodson, Betty (1974) *Liberating Masturbation*: A Meditation on Self Love Dodson, Publisher and Distribution, New York.

Dorner, S. (1977) Sexual Interest and Activity in Adolescents with Spina Bifida *Journal of Child Psychology and Psychiatry,* 18.

Friday, Nancy (1975) *Forbidden Flowers* Pocket Books, New York.

_____ (1976) *My Secret Garden* Pocket Books, New York.

Gordenk, Anita (1976) Motherhood and a Less-than-Perfect Child *Maternal-Child Nursing Journal*, 5:2.

Gordon, Sol Sexual Rights for the People Who Happen to be Handicapped. Center on Human Policy, Syracuse, NY.

Hatcher, Robert A., M.D., Stewart, Gary K., Stewart, Felicia, M.D., Guest, Felicia, Schwartz, David W., and Jones, Stephanie A. (1980) *Contraceptive Technology, 1980-1981* Irvington Publishers, Inc., New York.

Heslinga, K., M.D. (1974) *Not Made Of Stone* Charles C. Thomas, Springfield, IL.

Hite, Shere (1977) *The Hite Report*: A Nationwide Study of Female Sexuality. Dell Publishing Co., New York.

Kalter, Suzy (March 16, 1981) Nice Girls Do, Says Expert Irene Kassorla, Whose New Best-Seller Tells Them How *People.*

Kolodny, Robert C., Masters, William H., Johnson, Virginia S. and Biggs, Mae A. (1979) *Textbook of Human Sexuality for Nurses* Little, Brown and Co., Boston.

Montagu, Ashley (1972) *Touching*: The Human Significance of the Skin Harper and Row, New York.

Moore, Jean (Spring, 1981) Can a Wheelchair-Bound Woman Have a Baby? *Accent on Living*, 25:4.

Neistadt, Maureen and Baker, Maureen F. (1978) A Program for Sex Counseling the Physically Disabled *The American Journal of Occupational Therapy*, 32:10.

Rosenblum, Art (1976) *The Natural Birth Control Book* Aquarian Research Foundation, Philadelphia, PA.

Skipper, J.K., Jr., Fink, S.L. and Hallenbeck, P.N. (1968) Physical Disability Among Married Women; Problems in the Husband Wife Relationship *Journal of Rehabilitation,* 34.

Strauss, Elaine M. (1979) *In My Heart I'm Still Dancing* Elaine M. Strauss, Publisher and Distributor, New Rochelle, NY.

Strongin, Lynn. (1980) *Bones and Kim* Spinsters, Ink, Argyle, NY.

Task Force on Concerns of Physically Disabled Women (1977) *Within Reach: Providing Family Planning Services to Physically Disabled Women* Planned Parenthood of Snohomish County, Inc., Everett, WA.

Tavris, Carol and Sadd, Susan (1977) *The Redbook Report on Female Sexuality* Delacorte Press, New York.

Vargo, J.W. (1979) The Disabled Wife and Mother: Suggested Goals for Family Counseling *Canadian Counsellor,* 13.

Wright, Loyd S. (1976) Chronic Grief: The Anguish of Being an Exceptional Parent *The Exceptional Child,* 23.3

Zilbergeld, Bernie, Ph.D. (1978) *Male Sexuality* Little, Brown and Co., New York.